OXIDATION MECHANISMS

FRONTIERS IN CHEMISTRY

Ronald Breslow and Martin Karplus, editors
Columbia University

THERMODYNAMICS OF SMALL SYSTEMS

T. L. HILL   *University of Oregon*

LECTURES ON THE QUANTUM THEORY OF
MOLECULAR ELECTRONIC STRUCTURE

R. G. PARR   *The Johns Hopkins University*

OXIDATION MECHANISMS: Applications to Organic Chemistry

R. STEWART   *University of British Columbia*

THE ROLE OF ACETATE IN BIOSYNTHESIS

J. H. RICHARDS   *California Institute of Technology*
J. B. HENDRICKSON   *Brandeis University*

OXIDATION MECHANISMS

Applications to Organic Chemistry

Ross Stewart *765470*

University of British Columbia

W. A. BENJAMIN, INC.   1964

New York   Amsterdam

OXIDATION MECHANISMS: *Applications to Organic Chemistry*

Library of Congress Catalog Card Number 63–19978
Manufactured in the United States of America

Final manuscript was received on 6 February 1963;
this volume was published on 20 January 1964.

The publisher is pleased to acknowledge the
assistance of Cecilia Duray-Bito, who
produced the illustrations, and William
Prokos, who designed the dust jacket.

W. A. BENJAMIN, INC.
New York, New York

Editors' Foreword

It has become increasingly clear that developments in chemistry are moving so rapidly that new means are needed to report the current status of active fields of research. The person who wishes to appreciate the significance of current research or who desires to enter a new field often requires some aid in negotiating the difficult path through the voluminous series of original articles. Attempts to provide the necessary guidance have been made by review journals and by edited volumes composed of chapters written by a number of experts. Unfortunately, the best research scientists have sometimes been unwilling to write the reviews. Furthermore, since the review journals usually do not form a part of a scientist's personal library, the existing articles have not had the desired availability to students and research workers. Although the edited volumes avoid the latter difficulty, they do so at the expense of serious time delays resulting from the participation of many authors; the books are often out of date upon publication.

To overcome these problems in scientific communication we have initiated the series "Frontiers in Chemistry." It is expected that the series will consist primarily of brief monographs written by active workers in the various fields of chemistry. These will not be exhaustive treatises so much as critical reviews, in which an author indicates his opinion of the current status and future direction of a field. It is also our intent to publish occasional collections of reprints with an evaluation of the relationship of the articles to the current status of the field. We hope that the resulting series of monographs and reprint volumes will provide authoritative summaries that are readily available to both students and research scientists.

v

Any advice that will assist us in this purpose will be greatly appreciated. We particularly welcome suggestions of fields that should be included in the series or authors who should be invited to contribute.

R. Breslow
M. Karplus

New York, New York
February 1963

Preface

Some elegant studies of chemical mechanism have been made in the last decade on oxidation processes. Standard works on organic reaction mechanisms have tended to exclude most of these processes however, and there is a clear need to place these reactions in proper perspective. The present book attempts to do this.

Although an oxidation necessarily involves a reduction, the reactions considered herein are, for the most part, those in which an organic substrate reacts with an oxidizing agent, often an inorganic molecule or ion. In many of these reactions, mechanistic parallels with the more familiar processes of organic chemistry are apparent. The first three chapters deal with organic oxidations in general terms; the next three with the mechanisms used by chromium(VI), manganese(VII), and other transition metal oxidants to lower their chemical potential by reaction with organic substrates. The organization of the remainder of the book is somewhat arbitrary and one chapter, that on glycol cleavage, is based on structural similarities in the substrate rather than on the reactions of a particular oxidant. The final chapter deals with an important and rapidly developing field—oxidation pathways in biochemical systems.

Some oxidation mechanisms, notably those involving organic peroxy compounds, have been very adequately treated in other books or in recent review articles. In these cases a short account of the chemistry is given and the reader referred elsewhere for more details. Furthermore, neither heterogeneous reactions nor oxidations in the gas phase, which are chiefly the concern of the physical chemist, is discussed. Within the limitations set for the scope of this book I have tried to provide a useful mechanistic picture of those oxidation reactions that are of interest to the organic chemist and the biochemist. Indeed, one might include the inorganic chemist in view of the important role played by inorganic reagents in many of these reactions.

I am most grateful to Professors R. Breslow, W. D. Closson, J. Halpern, and K. B. Wiberg who read much of the manuscript and made invaluable suggestions. Conversation and correspondence with Professors C. A. Bunton, H. Kwart, J. Roček, and F. H. Westheimer are also gratefully acknowledged. I am also grateful for the help and encouragement of the charming lady who, among other things, typed the manuscript.

Ross Stewart

October 1963
Vancouver, Canada

Contents

CONTENTS

chapter
one

The Meaning
of Oxidation

The term *oxidation* has been part of common chemical usage since the time of Lavoisier. During that period of close to two centuries, several different definitions of the term have been offered. Transfer of oxygen, transfer of hydrogen, transfer of electrons—these have been the most commonly given descriptions of the oxidative and reductive processes. The laudable scientific desire to generalize has resulted in the last being the favored definition at the present time. Yet each of the above descriptions is the one that is most suitable for one of the following reactions:

$$Cu^+ + Ag^+ \rightarrow Cu^{++} + Ag$$

$$CH_3CHO + H_2O_2 \rightarrow CH_3CO_2H + H_2O$$

$$HCO_2H + C_6H_5CH{=}CH_2 \rightarrow CO_2 + C_6H_5CH_2CH_3$$

The curious aspect of this is that, despite the diverse chemistry of these reactions, even a neophyte chemist recognizes immediately that each is an example of what we call *oxidation* and *reduction*.

The common link between oxidizing agents is the fact that they all tend to produce the same alteration in compounds of the opposite type, i.e., those we call *reducing agents*. The corresponding situation holds for reducing agents. The reducing agents above, Cu^+, CH_3CHO, and HCO_2H, all produce the same products as in the above equations, that is, Cu^{++}, CH_3CO_2H, and CO_2, when acted on by a strong oxidizing agent, such as permanganate. Certainly cuprous ion loses an electron during the reaction, but a loss of electrons from acetaldehyde and formic acid can be formulated only in a very artificial way. It is also true that

1

there is electron reorganization in the conversion of acetaldehyde to acetic acid and styrene to ethylbenzene, but this is a common feature of all chemical processes.

Why is it that the powerful oxidants, $CrO_4^=$, MnO_4^-, VO_2^+, Co^{3+}, etc., all tend to cause the same alterations in organic molecules, e.g., the progression from primary alcohol to aldehyde to carboxylic acid to carbon dioxide—changes that obviously remove hydrogen atoms from carbon and/or add oxygen atoms to carbon? The problem of lowering the chemical potential of a system containing, say, a primary alcohol and potassium permanganate is not simply the transfer of electrons from the alcohol to the permanganate. The latter is willing enough to add one or more electrons to its unfilled orbitals, but the alcohol would then be converted to a cation of high energy indeed. The permanganate, in fact, has more than one choice; it can also, for example, accept a hydrogen atom from some hydrogen donor, or it can give up an oxygen atom to some suitable receiver.

$$MnO_4^- + e \to MnO_4^=$$

$$MnO_4^- + H\cdot \to HMnO_4^-$$

$$MnO_4^- \to MnO_3^- + O$$

Any of these three processes would be expected to lower the potential energy of the system. We say that these three processes all reduce the manganese from an oxidation state of $+7$ to an oxidation state of $+6$ in the first two cases and to $+5$ in the third. This assignment of oxidation states is based on the reasonable, and yet arbitrary, exclusion of proton transfers, hydroxyl-ion transfers, and oxide-ion transfers from the category of reactions that we call oxidations. That is, $HMnO_4^-$ and $MnO_4^=$ are in the same state of oxidation, because the former is converted to the latter by proton loss; the ion MnO_4^{3-} is in the same oxidation state as MnO_3^-, because it can be converted to the latter by oxide-ion loss.

The transfer of any hydrogen species other than the proton, the transfer of any oxygen species other than oxide or hydroxide ion, the transfer of any chlorine species other than chloride ion—any of these will cause what we call oxidation or reduction to take place. It is, of course, no coincidence that these are the normal, stable, ionic forms of these elements. Electron transfer, alone, will also cause a change in the oxidation state of the donor and recipient, but much of the work of the last decade in the field has served to show that electron transfer, per se, is by no means the only, nor even the favored, route used by such powerful oxidants as permanganate ion and chromic acid to lower their chemical potential.

It is possible to set up a set of oxidation states for both organic and inorganic reagents. Thus, ethane to ethanol (or ethylene) to acetaldehyde to acetic acid to carbon dioxide represents conversion to different oxidation levels, as does MnO_4^- to $MnO_4^=$ to MnO_3^- to MnO_2 to Mn^{3+} to Mn^{++}. (The question of equivalent weights is treated in the next chapter.) An oxidation or a reduction will be any reaction that converts one compound to a different oxidation state. Electron transfer will accomplish this for both organic and inorganic reagents *if* the subsequent or concomitant atomic and molecular reorganization, which must often be considered, is of the type mentioned earlier; i.e., hydrogen migration as a proton, oxygen as oxide or hydroxide ion, chlorine as chloride, etc.

This leads us to the definition of oxidation that will be used herein: An oxidation and a reduction has occurred in a chemical reaction if the products differ from the reactants in a way that cannot be accounted for simply by an exchange of protons, hydroxide ions, halide ions, alkali metal ions, ammonium ions, amide ions, etc., or, what is equivalent, by an exchange of water, hydrogen halide, ammonia, etc. This definition accommodates electron transfer, hydrogen-atom transfer, hydride transfer, chlorine-atom or chlorinium-ion transfer, and many others. It specifies no reaction mechanism. Subsequent chapters of this book will be devoted to an examination of the evidence accumulated in the studies of the mechanisms of many of these processes.

OXIDATIVE AND NONOXIDATIVE PATHS

Frequently, two reagents can react in more than one way, yielding several different sets of product. This situation is, of course, most familiar to synthetic organic chemists, but it can also arise in reactions between very simple molecules. If one examines by means of isotopic tracers the exchange reaction between SO_2 and SO_3, one can write several reasonable reaction paths (a, b, c, d) on the assumption that the only intermediates would be the known ions $SO_3^=$, SO^{++}, $SO_4^=$, and SO_2^{++}. The former pair would be expected to be in rapid equilibrium with SO_2 (oxidation state of $+4$), and the latter pair with SO_3 (oxidation state of $+6$). The following reaction paths, Eq. (1), are then possible: (a) Transfer of $O^=$ from SO_2 to SO_3; (b) transfer of $O^=$ from SO_3 to SO_2; (c) transfer of an oxygen atom from SO_3 to SO_2; (d) transfer of a pair of electrons from SO_2 to SO_3. Reaction paths (a) and (b) produce no change in the state of oxidation of the sulfur; paths (c) and (d) cause the sulfur atoms to exchange their oxidation state. Norris[1] has discussed the

1. F. H. Norris, *J. Phys. Chem.*, **63**, 383 (1959).

exchange of both sulfur and oxygen in the SO_2-SO_3 system; the oxygen exchange is extremely fast and the sulfur exchange is extremely slow ($t_{1/2} = 1,100$ days at $132°$). Reaction paths (c) and (d) must proceed via very high-energy transition states, whereas either (a) or (b) must have a low-energy transition state. The most reasonable structures

$$
*SO_2 + SO_3
\begin{array}{l}
\xrightarrow{(a)} *SO^{++} + SO_4^{=} \searrow \\
\xrightarrow{(b)} *SO_3^{=} + SO_2^{++} \nearrow *SO_2 + SO_3 \\
\xrightarrow{(c)} *SO_3 + SO_2 \\
\xrightarrow{(d)} *SO_2^{++} + SO_3^{=} \nearrow *SO_3 + SO_2
\end{array}
\tag{1}
$$

for the transition states are (I) and (II), which represent only the atom locations and are not intended to indicate bond order or charge distribution. Transition state (I) would serve for reactions (b) and (c) and probably (d) (see Chapter 6 for a discussion of bridged intermediates in electron-transfer reactions). The dotted lines show the positions of cleavage in the transition state for the three cases. If (I) is symmetrical,

(I)   (II)

it would lead to both sulfur and oxygen exchange, and hence is eliminated. On the other hand, (II) allows oxygen exchange, but not sulfur exchange, and is presumably the low-energy transition state, i.e., the one for path (a). It is not surprising that this involves oxide-ion transfer from a weaker acid, SO_2, to a stronger acid, SO_3.

A somewhat analogous situation holds for the oxidation of nitrite ion by hypochlorite ion.[2] This has been shown to proceed via oxygen-atom transfer[3] from OCl^- to NO_2^-.

$$NO_2^- + OCl^- \rightarrow [O_2N—O|—Cl]^= \rightarrow NO_3^- + Cl^-$$

2. M. Anbar and H. Taube, *J. Am. Chem. Soc.*, **80**, 1073 (1958).
3. The term *atom transfer* has been used for want of a better term to describe oxidations such as this that proceed with transfer of atoms or groups from oxidant to reductant, and vice versa (R. Stewart, *Experientia*, **1959**, 401). Neutrality of the transferred unit is not implied, i.e., Cl^+ and H^- transfers can be classed as atom-transfer reactions.

The transition state in this case cleaves as indicated to produce nitrate and chloride ions. It is reasonable that the scission should occur in this way rather than as O_2N—O—|Cl to produce the higher-energy ions NO_3^{3-} and Cl^+. These, in turn, would hydrolyze to the starting materials NO_2^- and OCl^-, in which case oxygen exchange would have occurred via $O^=$ transfer without any attendant oxidation and reduction. The distinction here between an oxidative and a nonoxidative path is obviously a small one, since the reactants are the same and the transition states are similar. The latter are, of course, not identical. Though their geometries will presumably be rather similar, the bond angles and distances and the electron distribution would certainly differ in the two cases.

　　The reaction of alkyl nitrate esters with base illustrates quite well the different ways in which a pair of reagents can interact. The four reaction paths shown in Eq. (2) all have transition states whose compositions are identical, but whose structures are different. One of them, the

$$RCH_2CH_2ONO_2 + CH_3O^- \begin{cases} RCH_2CH_2OCH_3 + NO_3^- \\ RCH_2CH_2O^- + CH_3ONO_2 \\ RCH{=}CH_2 + NO_3^- + CH_3OH \\ RCH_2C\!\!\begin{smallmatrix}O\\ \\H\end{smallmatrix} + NO_2^- + CH_3OH \end{cases} \qquad (2)$$

last, would normally be considered an oxidation-reduction reaction; the other three would not. The first set of products results from a nucleophilic displacement at the α-carbon; the second, from a nucleophilic displacement at nitrogen; the third, from proton abstraction from the β-carbon; the fourth, from proton abstraction from the α-carbon. The last process produces nitrite ion plus an aldehyde. The free energies of activation for the four paths will depend on the usual factors—solvent, temperature, the nature of the nucleophile, the structure of the alkyl group, and so on. Since the initial ester and the products of the other reactions above would normally be considered to be in the same oxidation state as alcohol and nitrate, it is clear that the fourth reaction of Eq. (2) has caused an oxidation and reduction to occur. Mechanistically, however, it is not unlike the other reaction paths.

chapter two | 1- and 2-Equivalent Oxidation Reactions

Equivalent weights of the common inorganic oxidants, such as manganese(VII) and chromium(VI), are usually defined as the formula weight divided by the formal number of electrons accepted by the species in the reaction in question. This, in the case of permanganate, can be any number from one to five. As we have seen earlier, this oxidant may in a given reaction either accept electrons or hydrogen *from* the reductant or donate oxygen *to* the reductant. Acceptance by the oxidant of one electron is equivalent to acceptance of a hydrogen atom, and acceptance of two electrons is equivalent to acceptance of a hydride ion, since the proton associated with the electrons in the two cases causes no change in the oxidation state. Acceptance of two electrons is also equivalent to a loss of an oxygen atom from the oxidant, and so on. Thus, reactions can be classified as 1-equivalent or 2-equivalent reactions according to the transfer that occurs during the process, and reagents can be similarly classified as 1- or 2-equivalent reagents. The terms 1- and 2-*electron transfer reagents* are sometimes used even though the reaction in question may not proceed by a direct electron transfer. (The possibility of a greater than 2-equivalent reaction will be discussed later.)

Michaelis[1-3] suggested that all oxidations of organic molecules proceed in two successive univalent steps via intermediate free radicals,

1. L. Michaelis, *Trans. Electrochem. Soc.*, **71**, 107 (1937).
2. L. Michaelis and M. Schubert, *Chem. Revs.*, **22**, 437 (1938).
3. L. Michaelis, in D. Green (ed.), *Currents in Biochemical Research*, Interscience, New York, 1946, p. 213.

and he showed, indeed, that semiquinones were intermediates in the oxidation of hydroquinone dianions by various reagents, e.g., ferricyanide, Eq. (1). In a similar way [Eq. (2)], the highly colored Wurster's

$$ \tag{1} $$

salts have been shown to be intermediates in the oxidation of p-phenylenediamine by bromine and other oxidants.[4-6] The universality of the Michaelis' postulate, however, has been adequately refuted,[7-9] since

$$ \tag{2} $$

there is also abundant evidence for the existence of 2-equivalent oxidation steps.[10] Many of the reactions described in later chapters are, in fact, of this type.

The tendency of different oxidizing agents to be reduced by either 1- or 2-equivalent steps was recognized by Kirk and Browne, who used the terms *mono-delectronator* and *di-delectronator*.[11] The distinction is based on the products observed when different oxidizing agents react with hydrazine or with sulfite. The 1-equivalent reagents tend to convert

4. C. Wurster and R. Sendtner, *Ber.*, **12**, 1803 (1879).
5. R. Wilstatter and J. Piccard, *Ber.*, **41**, 1458 (1908).
6. L. Michaelis, M. P. Schubert, and S. Granick, *J. Am. Chem. Soc.*, **61**, 1981 (1939).
7. F. H. Westheimer, in W. P. McElroy and B. Glass (eds.), *The Mechanism of Enzyme Action*, Johns Hopkins, Baltimore, 1954, p. 321.
8. J. Halpern, *Can. J. Chem.*, **37**, 148 (1959).
9. W. von E. Doering and T. C. Aschner, *J. Am. Chem. Soc.*, **75**, 393 (1953).
10. It should be recognized, however, that Michaelis' pioneering work on 1-equivalent oxidation reactions was of the greatest importance. See, for example, B. Chance in M. S. Blois, Jr., H. W. Brown, R. M. Lemmon, R. O. Lindblom, and M. Weissbluth (eds.), *Free Radicals in Biological Systems*, Academic, New York, 1961, pp. 1-14.
11. R. E. Kirk and A. W. Browne, *J. Am. Chem. Soc.*, **50**, 337 (1928).

Table 2-1   *Oxidizing agents*

1-Equivalent	2-Equivalent[a]	1,2-Equivalent
Ce^{IV}	Tl^{III}	Cr^{VI}
Co^{III}	H_2O_2	Mn^{VII}
Fe^{III}	X_2	Pt^{IV}
OH	XO^-	V^V
	XO_3^-	

[a] X = halogen.

the latter to dithionate (presumably via SO_3^{-}), and the 2-equivalent reagents tend to produce sulfate (either directly or via SO_3). Higginson and Marshall have classified (Table 2-1) several inorganic oxidizing agents according to their preference for a 1- or 2-equivalent reduction step.[12] The 1,2-equivalent reagents appear to react readily by either route, depending on the particular reducing agent involved. It is not surprising that the stable oxidation steps of the 1-equivalent reagents differ by one unit. The distinction is not a rigid one, and of the 2-equivalent reagents above, halogen for one, is known to react at times by 1-equivalent steps, e.g., in radical-catalyzed brominations a radical abstracts a bromine atom from Br_2.

Organic compounds, with certain important exceptions, tend to avoid reactions requiring 1-equivalent steps. This is because stable organic compounds normally do not have unpaired electrons, i.e., they are not radicals. In some cases, however, either because of unusual stabilizing features in the radical—resonance stabilization in the case of Michaelis' semiquinones or Wurster's salts—or because of the existence of a chain-reaction path, radicals are known to be reaction intermediates. Individual steps in these reactions might be classified as 1-equivalent reactions whether or not over-all oxidation occurs.

PRINCIPLE OF EQUI-VALENCE CHANGE

Shaffer,[13] in 1933, suggested that a redox reaction between a 2-equivalent reagent and a 1-equivalent reagent would be slow compared with a reaction between two reagents of the same type. In support of this

12. W. C. E. Higginson and J. W. Marshall, *J. Chem. Soc.*, **1957**, 447.
13. P. A. Shaffer, *J. Am. Chem. Soc.*, **55**, 2169 (1933).

idea is the fact that reactions such as the one between Tl^+ and Ce^{4+} to give Tl^{3+} and Ce^{3+} are slow. The only routes for such a reaction would be either a termolecular reaction between 2 molecules of the 1-equivalent reagent (Ce^{IV}) and 1 molecule of the 2-equivalent reagent (Tl^I) or a two-step process involving an unstable oxidation state of one or the other components. (Halpern [8] has argued that, despite the less favorable entropy of a termolecular reaction, it may in some cases be the better alternative because of a lower activation energy.) Since the 1- and 2-equivalent classification for reagents is not a rigid one, it follows that exceptions to the principle of equi-valence change will be found.

The principle of equi-valence change can be readily applied to organic reactions. One-equivalent reagents, radicals, will almost always react with each other in preference to 2-equivalent reagents, i.e., non-radicals. The exceptions are those cases in which steric effects prevent radical coupling, or structural effects prevent disproportionation. (Radical coupling is a minor side reaction in most chain reactions only because the steady-state concentration of radicals is very small.)

Perchloryl fluoride, $FClO_3$, can be classed as both a 1- and a 2-equivalent reagent, since it causes both a 1- and a 2-equivalent oxidation of 2,6-dimethyl phenoxide ion, evidently by a nucleophilic-displacement path and an electron-abstraction path[14] [Eq. (3)].

$$(3)$$

3-EQUIVALENT CHANGE

It has been suggested that changes of oxidation number greater than two will not occur in a single step, and it is true that there appear to be no known examples of such a reaction. A simultaneous 3-electron transfer is unlikely, and the transfer of such unusual species as $H^=$,

14. A. S. Kende and P. MacGregor, *J. Am. Chem. Soc.*, **83**, 4197 (1961).

Cl^{++}, or O^+ does not seem an attractive alternative. However, for a system whose only stable oxidation states differ by three units, a 3-equivalent reaction may be possible. There are few likely looking pairs of redox reactants in this category, but one for which such a path seems reasonable is the exchange between nitric acid [nitrogen(V)] and nitric oxide [nitrogen(II)] in acid solution. Nitronium ion is known to be in equilibrium with nitric acid, and any reaction between it and nitric oxide could conceivably take the following course:

$$\overset{*}{N}O_2{}^+ + NO \rightarrow [O\overset{*}{N}ONO]^+ \rightarrow \overset{*}{N}O + NO_2{}^+$$

The bracketed radical ion above might represent a transition state or an intermediate with an appreciable lifetime. The latter is not unlikely, since a reasonable set of valence bond structures can be written for it.

$$[O{=}\overset{+}{N}{-}O{-}N{=}O \leftrightarrow O{=}N{-}O{-}\overset{+}{N}{=}O \leftrightarrow O{=}N{-}\overset{+}{O}{=}N{-}O{\cdot} \leftrightarrow$$
$${\cdot}O{-}N{=}\overset{+}{O}{-}N{=}O]$$

ELECTRON TRANSFER BETWEEN ORGANIC IONS AND MOLECULES

Electron exchange between organic anions and their neutral analogs will be fast only if extensive atomic reorganization is not required for the reaction to take place.

$$^*Z^- + Z \rightleftharpoons {}^*Z + Z^-$$

or

$$Z^- + Z \rightleftharpoons 2Z^-$$

Furthermore, this reaction will be important only for those ions, such as ketyl anions[15-17] or quinone dianions,[2, 18-20] whose neutral forms are reasonably stable [Eqs. (4)].

The Franck-Condon principle, which states that electronic transitions are very much faster than atomic motions, has found important application in the study of the exchange between pairs of inorganic ions,

15. F. C. Adam and S. I. Weissman, *J. Am. Chem. Soc.*, **80**, 1518 (1958).
16. W. Schlenk and R. Ochs, Ber. **49**, 608 (1916).
17. G. Wittig and D. Wittenberg, *Ann.*, **606**, 1 (1957).
18. T. H. James and A. Weissberger, *J. Am. Chem. Soc.*, **60**, 98 (1938).
19. J. H. Baxendale and H. R. Hardy, *Trans. Faraday Soc.*, **49**, 1433 (1953).
20. H. Diebler, M. Eigen, and P. Matthies, *Z. Naturforsch.*, **16B**, 629 (1961).

such as Fe^{++} and Fe^{3+}.[21,22] The normal solvation spheres about each of these ions is different, since the triply charged ferric anion will be more heavily and tightly solvated than will the doubly charged ferrous ion. Electron exchange, then, requires a reorganization of the solvation spheres about both ions, and this limits the rate of the electron transfer.[23]

$$Ar_2\overset{.}{C}\text{—}O^- + Ar_2C\text{=}O \rightleftharpoons Ar_2C\text{=}O + Ar_2\overset{.}{C}\text{—}O^-$$

(4)

Organic ions are usually highly delocalized, and solvation changes are unlikely to play as important a role in determining the rate of electron exchange as they do with many inorganic ions. However, an interesting conclusion emerges from the study of the electron transfer between benzophenone and the sodium salt of the corresponding ketyl radical anion. This exchange reaction has been studied by Adam and Weissman by electron-spin resonance.[15]

$$(C_6H_5)_2C\text{=}O + (C_6H_5)_2\overset{.}{C}\text{—}O^-Na^+ \rightleftharpoons (C_6H_5)_2\overset{.}{C}\text{—}O^-Na^+ + (C_6H_5)_2C\text{=}O$$

They found that the spin-resonance spectrum of the radical is split by the nuclear spin of the nearby sodium-23 nucleus. In the presence of excess benzophenone, the spectrum of the radical is altered because of the increased rate of exchange of the odd electron between the ketyl and ketone. A detailed analysis of the spectrum reveals that the electron that is transferred is accompanied by a sodium ion. This is analogous to the solvation changes that accompany the ferrous-ferric exchange, since transfer of an electron from a ketyl radical anion to a benzophenone molecule requires the cation to be nearby. Otherwise, the products would be in a high-energy state with the newly formed radical anion lacking a cation neighbor, and vice versa. Since the over-all free energy change for the reaction must be zero, this is impossible.

21. W. F. Libby, *J. Phys. Chem.*, **56**, 863 (1952).
22. R. A. Marcus, *Discussions Faraday Soc.*, **29**, 21 (1960).
23. For a more detailed discussion of electron exchange between inorganic ions, see Ref. 8 and F. Basolo and R. G. Pearson, *Mechanism of Inorganic Reactions*, Wiley, New York, 1958, pp. 303ff.

An exchange reaction between a charge-delocalized ion and its neutral molecule will also be accompanied by bond-length changes and often by bond-angle changes. These, too, are analogous to the solvation-sphere alterations that limit the rate of electron transfer between simple inorganic ions.

Electron exchange between various other unsaturated organic compounds and their corresponding anions has been studied.[24-26]

Levitt has suggested that electron-pair transfer within an oxidant-reductant coordinate complex is the common basis for organic oxidations in acid solution.[27] Subsequent work has revealed, however, that a variety of reaction paths exist, and these are described in later chapters.

24. T. J. Katz and H. L. Strauss, *J. Chem. Phys.*, **32**, 1873 (1960).
25. G. A. Russell, E. G. Janzen, and E. T. Strom, *J. Am. Chem. Soc.*, **84**, 4155 (1962); G. A. Russell and E. G. Janzen, *J. Am. Chem. Soc.*, **84**, 4153 (1962); and references therein.
26. M. T. Jones and S. I. Weissman, *J. Am. Chem. Soc.*, **84**, 4269 (1962).
27. L. S. Levitt, *J. Org. Chem.*, **20**, 1297 (1955).

The Breaking of Carbon-Hydrogen and Carbon-Carbon Bonds

chapter three

The vast majority of organic oxidations involve the rupture of carbon-hydrogen or carbon-carbon bonds. Both hydrogen and carbon are, generally speaking, poor leaving groups because of the extremely high energy of the three possible forms, cation, radical, and anion. In the case of hydrogen, most of the energy for bond breaking must come from simultaneous bond making by the reagent that is removing the proton, the hydrogen atom, or the hydride ion. In the case of carbon-carbon bonds, stabilizing features may be present in the eliminated group, which reduce the need for bond formation with another molecule.

A carbon-hydrogen bond may be broken homolytically by hydrogen-atom abstraction or heterolytically by either proton or hydride abstraction.

HOMOLYTIC C—H BOND CLEAVAGE

The unassisted cracking of a carbon-hydrogen bond requires 70 to 100 kcal mole^{-1}, and displacement of a hydrogen atom by radical attack on carbon is also an energetically unfavorable process. Virtually all

13

homolytic cleavages of C—H bonds that occur under normal conditions, then, are displacements by radicals on hydrogen.

$$R\cdot + H-\overset{|}{\underset{|}{C}}- \;\rightarrow\; R-H + \cdot\overset{|}{\underset{|}{C}}-$$

Molecular oxygen is particularly effective at insinuating itself into this reaction scheme to produce oxidized products by the following two-step chain:

$$-\overset{|}{\underset{|}{C}}\cdot + O_2 \;\rightarrow\; -\overset{|}{\underset{|}{C}}-O-O\cdot$$

$$-\overset{|}{\underset{|}{C}}-O-O\cdot + H-\overset{|}{\underset{|}{C}}- \;\rightarrow\; -\overset{|}{\underset{|}{C}}-O-OH + \cdot\overset{|}{\underset{|}{C}}-$$

The thorough studies that have been made of these autoxidation-chain reactions, together with studies of the polymerization process, have provided us with most of our knowledge of the mode of homolytic C—H bond cleavage.

Hydrogen-atom abstraction occurs most easily at position alpha to unsaturated groups, particularly at allylic positions, because of resonance stabilization of the resulting radical. The autoxidation of cyclohexene, for example, can be initiated by the adventitious presence of traces of radicals, such as those produced by the thermal decomposition of peroxides or azobisnitriles.

$$\overset{O}{\overset{\|}{R}}\overset{O}{\overset{\|}{C}}OO\overset{}{C}R \;\rightarrow\; 2RCO_2\cdot \;\rightarrow\; 2R\cdot + 2CO_2$$

$$R_2\overset{|}{\underset{CN}{C}}N{=}N\overset{|}{\underset{CN}{C}}R_2 \;\rightarrow\; 2R_2\overset{\bullet}{C}CN + N_2$$

Direct thermal initiation by hydrogen-atom abstraction by molecular oxygen may sometimes occur, but it is difficult to detect because of the ubiquity of traces of peroxidic impurity.[1]

Ionizing radiation, or even visible light, may also serve as an initiator for autoxidation. Photosensitized oxidation of olefins occurs [Eq. (1)] by means of a cyclic intermediate in which double-bond migration takes place.[1-4]

$$-\underset{|}{\overset{H}{C}}-C=C-+O_2 \rightarrow \left[\begin{array}{c} \end{array} \right] \rightarrow -C=C-\underset{|}{\overset{HO_2}{C}}- \qquad (1)$$

Hydrogen atoms at benzylic positions are also readily removed. Benzaldehyde, toluene, and tetralin all produce radicals stabilized by resonance interaction with the aromatic ring.

Tertiary hydrogens in nonconjugating positions are next in order of ease of removal, followed by secondary and primary hydrogens. Thus, decalin forms a peroxide readily at the 9-position.

1. K. U. Ingold, *Chem. Revs.*, **61**, 563 (1961).
2. E. H. Farmer, *Trans. Faraday Soc.*, **42**, 228 (1946).
3. N. A. Khan, *Can. J. Chem.*, **32**, 1149 (1954).
4. See also page 161.

With sufficiently reactive reagents, hydrogen-atom abstraction can occur from the α-position of alcohols, e.g.,[5]

$$CH_3CH_2OH + H\cdot \rightarrow CH_3\overset{\cdot}{C}HOH + H_2$$

The abstracting radical is here a hydrogen atom (generated by X irradiation). One of the unusual aspects of this reaction is the very large isotope effect found for the reaction of CH_3CD_2OH: $k_H/k_D = 17$. Isotope effects as large as this have been found in only one other case, the permanganate oxidation of fluoro alcohols, and there, too, hydrogen abstraction may be occurring (page 67).

The above discussion of homolytic C—H bond cleavage is, of necessity, highly abbreviated. The reader is referred to other works for a comprehensive discussion of reactions that proceed by this process.[5-8]

HETEROLYTIC C—H BOND CLEAVAGE

A carbon-hydrogen bond can be cleaved heterolytically by either hydride or proton abstraction. The former process always results in an oxidation—the latter only if it is accompanied by certain changes elsewhere in the molecule, as will be seen in the subsequent discussion.

Proton Abstraction

An example of an oxidation reaction in which the rate-controlling step is proton abstraction is the so-called *carbonyl-elimination (Eco2) reaction* that benzyl nitrate undergoes under the influence of base to produce benzaldehyde and nitrite ion. [This is the redox path of the reaction referred to on page 5 and is a model for the chromate ester decomposition discussed in the next chapter.]

$$C_6H_5CH_2ONO_2 + EtO^- \rightarrow C_6H_5CHO + NO_2^- + EtOH$$

The elegant studies that have been made of this reaction, chiefly by Baker and Heggs[9] and Buncel and Bourns,[10] leave little doubt as to the reaction mechanism. The latters' work illustrates the multiple use of

5. C. Lifshitz and G. Stein, *J. Chem. Soc.*, **1962**, 3706.
6. C. Walling, *Free Radicals in Solution*, Wiley, New York, 1957.
7. J. K. Kochi, *J. Am. Chem. Soc.*, **84**, 2121 (1962).
8. The coupling phenols brought about by 1-equivalent oxidants is discussed by C. H. Hassall and A. I. Scott in W. D. Ollis (ed.), *Chemistry of Natural Phenolic Compounds*, Pergamon Press, London, 1961, p. 119.
9. J. W. Baker and T. G. Heggs, *J. Chem. Soc.*, **1955**, 616.
10. E. Buncel and A. N. Bourns, *Can. J. Chem.*, **38**, 2457 (1960).

isotope effects. They found a deuterium-isotope effect, k_H/k_D, of 5.04 ± 0.25 at $60°$ (corresponding to a value of about 6.1 at $25°$) for the reaction of $C_6H_5CD_2ONO_2$, showing clearly that α-carbon–hydrogen bond rupture is occurring in the rate-controlling step.[11,12] A nitrogen-15–isotope effect, k_{14}/k_{15}, of 1.0196 ± 0.0006 at $30°$ was also found. This is a large value for nitrogen, showing that oxygen-nitrogen bond rupture is also well advanced in the transition state. (The precision of the nitrogen-isotope effect is the more remarkable in that enriched isotopic compounds were not used—the departure from natural abundance as the reaction proceeds was followed mass-spectrometrically.) This reaction must be a concerted elimination process with the transition state shown in structure (I).

$$
\underset{(I)}{
\overset{\displaystyle C_6H_5}{
\underset{\displaystyle H}{
EtO\text{---}H\text{---}\underset{|}{\overset{|}{C}}\overset{\delta-}{=}O\text{---}NO_2}}}
$$

The effect of substituents in the aromatic ring is also in accord with this mechanism.[9] Loss of the proton from the benzylic carbon should be facilitated by electron-withdrawing substituents in the ring; i.e., the Hammett reaction constant ρ (rho) in the equation $\log(k/k_0) = \sigma\rho$, should be large and positive.[13] The experimental value shown in Eq. (2) is an entirely reasonable one for this mechanism.

$$\rho = -3.4, \; B = C_2H_5O^- \tag{2}$$

The ability of esters in general to undergo the base-promoted oxidation-reduction described above for benzyl nitrate has been discussed by Anbar et al.[14] They point out that an ester RCH_2OZ will decompose by the redox path A only if Z is stable in the lower oxidation

11. K. B. Wiberg, *Chem. Revs.*, **55,** 713 (1955).
12. L. Melander, *Isotope Effects on Reaction Rates*, Ronald, New York, 1960.
13. L. P. Hammett, *Physical Organic Chemistry*, McGraw-Hill, New York, 1940, p. 185.
14. M. Anbar, I. Dostrovsky, D. Samuel, and A. D. Yoffe, *J. Chem. Soc.*, **1954**, 3603.

state, i.e., if Z^- tends to be more stable than OZ^-. Otherwise, path B is followed [see Eq. (3)]. Chromate, hypochlorite, and bromate esters $(Z = CrO_3H, Cl, BrO_2),$[15] thus usually follow path A, whereas acetate and nitrite esters $(Z = CH_3CO, NO)$ will follow path B.

$$RCH_2OZ + OH^- \xrightarrow{\begin{array}{c} A \\ \\ \\ B \end{array}} \begin{cases} RCHO + H_2O + Z^- \\ \\ RCH_2OH + OZ^- \end{cases} \tag{3}$$

The ability of a tertiary alkyl ester of an inorganic acid to function as an oxidizing agent for alcohols depends on a second characteristic in addition to that described above: The ester must be able to undergo transesterification with the alcohol.[14] Chromate esters possess both these properties, and compounds, such as di-t-butyl chromate, are most useful oxidants for alcohols, particularly since they are soluble in organic solvents.

Hydride Abstraction

Turning next to hydride abstraction from carbon, we find several particularly clear examples of this type of bond cleavage. The mechanism of the base-catalyzed carbinol–carbonyl equilibrium has been examined by Doering and Aschner,[16] who showed that the reaction is completely unaffected by radicals, such as Bindschedler's Green, $(Me_2NC_6H_4)_2N\cdot,$[17] suggesting that the reaction is a 2-equivalent oxidation. Furthermore, the racemization of an optically active primary or secondary alcohol by base requires the presence of a carbonyl compound. Thus, $(-)$-2-methyl-butanol-1 on refluxing with 5 mole per cent of its sodium salt undergoes no racemization at all; when a few per cent of benzophenone is added, fairly rapid racemization occurs [Eq. (4)]. When this reaction is run in a deuterated solvent, no deuterium is found on the carbon atom that is being oxidized and reduced.

These results show that the alcohol is oxidized in a 2-equivalent step to the aldehyde (which is known to racemize in base) and is then reduced

15. C. A. Grob and H. J. Schmid, *Helv. Chim. Acta*, **36**, 1763 (1953); M. Anbar and D. Ginsburg, *Chem. Revs.*, **54**, 925 (1954); L. Farkas and N. Uri, *Proc. Intern. Congr. Pure and Appl. Chem.*, **11**, 449 (1947); *C.A.* **45**, 1498 (1951).
16. W. von E. Doering and T. C. Aschner, *J. Am. Chem. Soc.*, **75**, 393 (1953).
17. Certain carbonyl compounds, such as anthraquinone, do react readily with this 1-equivalent reagent. See Ref. 16 and A. Geake and J. T. Lemon, *Trans. Faraday Soc.*, **34**, 1409 (1938).

$$CH_3$$
$$C_2H_5\text{—}\underset{\underset{H}{|}}{\overset{\overset{CH_3}{|}}{C}}\text{—}CH_2OH \xrightarrow[RO^-]{(C_6H_5)_2C=O} C_2H_5\text{—}\underset{\underset{H}{|}}{\overset{\overset{CH_3}{|}}{C}}\text{—}CHO \xrightarrow[RO^-]{(C_6H_5)_2C=O}$$

optically active   racemizes

$$C_2H_5\text{—}\underset{\underset{H}{|}}{\overset{\overset{CH_3}{|}}{C}}\text{—}CH_2OH \qquad (4)$$

racemic

in another 2-equivalent step without intervention of solvent hydrogens. A hydride transfer from alkoxide ion to carbonyl compound is evidently the path [Eq. (5)] for the oxidation and reduction that cause the equilibration.[18]

$$R_2CHO^- + R_2'C{=}O \rightarrow \left[\begin{array}{c} R \quad\quad R' \\ \overset{\delta-}{O}{=}\underset{\underset{R}{|}}{\overset{\overset{|}{}}{C}}\text{---}H\text{---}\underset{\underset{R'}{|}}{\overset{\overset{|}{}}{C}}\overset{\delta-}{{=}O} \end{array}\right] \rightarrow R_2C{=}O + R_2'CHO^- \qquad (5)$$

The carbinol-carbonyl equilibrium is also catalyzed by strong acids, and one can write reasonable mechanisms, similar to Eq. (5), in which hydride is transferred from neutral alcohol to protonated carbonyl instead of from alkoxide to neutral alcohol.[19]

$$\overset{+OH}{\underset{|}{\overset{\|}{-C}}} \quad \overset{OH}{\underset{|}{\overset{|}{(H\text{—})C\text{—}}}} \rightarrow \overset{OH}{\underset{|}{\overset{|}{-C\text{—}H}}} + \overset{+OH}{\underset{|}{\overset{\|}{C\text{—}}}}$$

When Lewis-acid catalysts, such as aluminum alkoxides, are used to interconvert alcohols and ketones (Meerwein-Pondorff-Oppenauer equilibrium), a cyclic mechanism [Eq. (6)] is believed to be operative.[20]

18. Benzyl alcohol–potassium hydroxide systems have been used to reduce aldehydes and highly polarizable olefins. The benzylate ion is presumably a hydride donor in these cases. See Y. Sprinzak, *J. Am. Chem. Soc.*, **78**, 466 (1956); L. Palfrey and S. Sabetay, *Compt. rend.*, **200**, 404 (1935); P. Mastagli, *Ann. chim.*, **11** (10), 281 (1938).
19. N. C. Deno, G. S. Saines, and M. Spangler, *J. Am. Chem. Soc.*, **84**, 3295 (1962).
20. R. B. Woodward, N. L. Wendler, and F. J. Brutschy, *J. Am. Chem. Soc.*, **67**, 1425 (1945).

These reactions are usually considered hydride transfers, because the metal atom will polarize the carbonyl group and will assist hydride addition to carbon. However, the question of identifying the mode of bond breaking and the direction of electron flow in cyclic transition states has been the subject of some controversy.[21, 22]

$$
\begin{array}{ccc}
\overset{\diagdown\text{Al}\diagup}{\underset{R\diagdown C}{O}\,\,O\,C\diagup R} & \left[\overset{\diagdown\text{Al}\diagup}{\underset{R\diagdown C}{O}\cdots H\cdots C\diagup R}\right] & \overset{\diagdown\text{Al}\diagup}{\underset{R\diagdown C}{O}\,\,O\,C\diagup R}
\end{array}
\tag{6}
$$

The question of cyclic vs. acyclic mechanisms arises again when one considers the Cannizzaro reaction, the base-catalyzed disproportionation of aldehydes that lack an α-hydrogen.

$$2ArCHO + OH^- \rightarrow ArCO_2^- + ArCH_2OH$$

This reaction is usually written [Eq. (7)] as a direct hydride transfer from an aldehyde-hydroxide adduct to a second mole of aldehyde, although an intramolecular mechanism [Eq. (8)] has occasionally been suggested.[23]

$$
ArCHO + OH^- \rightleftharpoons Ar-\overset{\displaystyle O^-}{\underset{\displaystyle OH}{C}}-H
\tag{7}
$$

$$
Ar-\overset{\displaystyle O^-}{\underset{\displaystyle OH}{C}}(-H) \quad \overset{O}{\underset{H}{\overset{\|}{C}}}-Ar \rightarrow
$$

$$ArCO_2H + ArCH_2OH \rightarrow ArCO_2^- + ArCH_2OH \tag{8}$$

In strongly basic solution, a second-order term in [OH$^-$] appears in the kinetics,[24] and there is general agreement that this reflects the increased

21. C. K. Ingold, *Structure and Mechanism in Organic Chemistry*, Cornell, Ithaca, N.Y., 1953, p. 596.
22. C. G. Swain, R. F. W. Bader, R. M. Esteve, Jr., and R. N. Griffin, *J. Am. Chem. Soc.*, **83**, 1951 (1961).
23. For a fuller discussion of the Cannizzaro and related reactions, see J. Hine, *Physical Organic Chemistry*, McGraw-Hill, New York, 1962, p. 267, and C. K. Ingold, Ref. 21, p. 704.
24. A. Eitel and G. Lock, *Monatsh.*, **72**, 392 (1939).

hydride-donor properties of the ion $ArCHO_2^=$, which will be present in small concentrations in these solutions [Eq. (9)].

$$\rightarrow ArCO_2^- + ArCH_2O^- \qquad (9)$$

Both the mechanisms written here are exact analogs of the base-catalyzed carbinol-carbonyl equilibrium considered earlier. A mechanism that does not seem to have been hitherto considered is the reaction of the aldehyde monoanion with a second molecule of aldehyde by a cyclic transition state. The last might be formed with the hydrogens being transferred together, rather than in two separate steps, with a consequent lowering of the activation barrier; i.e., the exothermicity of the second reaction in the mechanism, as it is usually written,

$$ArCO_2H + ArCH_2O^- \rightarrow ArCO_2^- + ArCH_2OH$$

might be used to advantage in the rate-controlling step [Eq. (10)]. Such a reaction is, of course, not possible with the dianion.

$$\rightarrow ArCO_2^- + \qquad (10)$$

Other reactions that are generally believed to proceed by a hydride-transfer mechanism are the following: The reduction of hindered ketones by Grignard reagents,[25] the Leuckart reduction of ketones by ammonium formate,[26] the reduction of enamines by formic acid,[27] the Sommelet conversion of primary alkyl halides to aldehydes,[28, 29] the hydrolysis of pyridine diarylboranes,[30] and many of the reactions of

25. G. E. Dunn and J. Warkentin, *Can. J. Chem.*, **34**, 75 (1956).
26. M. L. Moore, in R. Adams (ed.), *Organic Reactions*, vol. V, Wiley, New York, 1949, p. 301.
27. N. J. Leonard and R. R. Sauers, *J. Am. Chem. Soc.*, **79**, 6210 (1957).
28. S. J. Angyal and R. C. Rassack, *J. Chem. Soc.*, **1949**, 2700.
29. S. J. Angyal, in R. Adams (ed.), *Organic Reactions*, vol. VIII, Wiley, New York, 1954, p. 197.
30. E. S. Lewis and R. H. Grinstein, *J. Am. Chem. Soc.*, **84**, 1158 (1962).

carbonium ions. The last are described in Chapter 10. A general review of hydride-transfer reactions has been made by Deno, Peterson, and Saines.[31]

Criteria for Distinguishing Proton and Hydride Abstractions

Lewis, Symons, and Hawthorne have put forth the suggestion that attack by an electrophile on a C—H bond will be more efficient if the attack is made, not along the extended bond axis, but rather at an angle to it.[32, 33] Repulsion between the proton and the electrophile will be somewhat reduced in this way, and partial electron transfer to the electrophile in the transition state will be facilitated. The triangular transition state that they visualize [Eq. (11)] involves partial bonding between the electrophile, the carbon atom of the substrate, and the transferred hydrogen.

$$E+ \overset{H}{\underset{\diagup C \diagdown}{|}} \rightarrow \left[E \overset{\diagup H}{\underset{\diagup C \diagdown}{\diagdown}} \right] \rightarrow E \overset{\diagup H}{\underset{\diagup C \diagdown}{|}} \tag{11}$$

Wagner-Meerwein rearrangements in which hydrogen is the migrating group are examples of 1,2-hydride shifts that must proceed by such a route [Eq. (12)]. The geometric restrictions placed on the transition state by the fact that the electrophile and the hydride donor are

$$RCH_2CH_2^+ \rightarrow \left[R\overset{\diagup H \diagdown}{CH}{-}CH_2 \right]^+ \rightarrow R\overset{+}{C}HCH_3 \tag{12}$$

adjacent atoms in the same molecule are thus pictured as factors favoring the reaction. An *inter*molecular hydride transfer, however, is unlikely to benefit as greatly from a triangular structure in which the proton is embedded in a bond between the electrophile and the hydride donor. In Eq. (12), this can be written as a triangular π complex

$$RCH \overset{H^+}{\underset{\uparrow}{=\!\!=}} CH_2$$

between an olefin and proton. In the case of hydride transfer between two atoms that are not bonded in the initial and final states, we should seek a model that will serve as well as the π complex does for the hydride transfer between bonded atoms.

31. N. C. Deno, H. J. Peterson, and G. S. Saines, *Chem. Revs.*, **60**, 7 (1960).
32. E. S. Lewis and M. C. R. Symons, *Quart. Revs. (London)*, **12**, 230 (1958).
33. M. F. Hawthorne and E. S. Lewis *J. Am. Chem. Soc.*, **80**, 4296 (1958).

A partial bond formed in the transition state between two orbitals on carbon, one in the electrophile, the other in the hydride donor, will be more like a sigma bond than a pi bond. The hydrogen bond is not a satisfactory model for a proton buried in a sigma bond between two first-row elements, since it, the hydrogen bond, contains one extra electron pair.

A few examples of 1,3-hydride shifts have been confirmed,[34-37] and it appears as if they occur with surprising ease. The 1,2-hydride shift

$$
\begin{array}{ccc}
CH_3CH_2CH_2NH_2 \xrightarrow{HNO_2} & & \nearrow CH_3\overset{+}{C}HCH_3 \\
& CH_3CH_2\overset{+}{C}H_2 & \\
CH_3CH_2CH_2O^- \xrightarrow{BCr_2} & & \searrow {}^+CH_2CH_2CH_3
\end{array}
\tag{13}
$$

appears to be favored by a factor of only about 10 in the case of Eq. (13).[34,35] The transition state for the 1,3-shifts must be that in structure (II).

$$
\begin{array}{c}
H_2 \\
\delta^+ \diagup \overset{C}{} \diagdown \delta^+ \\
H_2C \diagdown \quad \diagup CH_2 \\
H
\end{array}
$$

(II)

Lewis and Symons point out that one of the consequences of a triangular transition state will be retention of the hydrogen-stretching mode in the transition state, which should lead in turn to a low deuterium-isotope effect.[32] They point out that, in such hydride-transfer reactions as the Cannizzaro reaction, the hydrolyses of triphenyl silane and of diphenylboranepyridine, and the alcohol–carbonium-ion reaction, very low isotope effects (< 2) are, in fact, found.

A nonlinear transition state may suffer from considerable steric strain if both the substituting reagent and the substrate are bulky molecules. Thus, in the hydride-exchange reaction between tertiary carbonium ions and the corresponding hydrocarbons, an attack along the carbon-carbon bond axis would have the advantage of reducing steric

34. P. S. Skell and I. Starer, *J. Am. Chem. Soc.*, **84**, 3962 (1962).
35. O. A. Reutov. and T. N. Shatkina, *Tetrahedron*, **18**, 237 (1962).
36. G. J. Karabatsos and C. E. Orzech, Jr., *J. Am. Chem. Soc.*, **84**, 2838 (1962).
37. A. C. Cope, G. A. Berchtold, P. E. Peterson, and S. H. Sharman, *J. Am. Chem. Soc.*, **82**, 6366 (1960).

strain in the transition state caused by nonbonded repulsions between the alkyl groups.

$$R_3C^+ + HCR_3 \rightarrow \left[R_3\overset{\delta+}{C}\text{---}H\text{---}\overset{\delta+}{C}R_3 \right] \rightarrow R_3CH + {}^+CR_3$$

Swain has suggested that proton and hydride transfers may be distinguished by examining the effect of substituents in the reacting molecules on the size of the isotope effect when deuterium is the transferred atom.[38] The basis for this distinction is the fact that a proton transfer differs from a hydride transfer in the possession of two extra electrons by the three-atom molecular orbital formed in the transition state.

$$R\text{---}H \quad :N \rightarrow [R\text{---}H\text{---}N] \rightarrow R: \quad H\text{---}N \qquad \text{proton transfer}$$

$$R\text{---}H \quad E \rightarrow [R\text{---}H\text{---}E] \rightarrow R \quad H\text{---}E \qquad \text{hydride transfer}$$

The molecule :N is a nucleophile with a filled nonbonded orbital; the molecule E is an electrophile with a low-energy unfilled orbital. One can assume for purposes of discussion that the transition state is formed by the overlap of a p orbital on R, a p orbital on N or E, and an s orbital on hydrogen. The extra electron pair required for proton transfer would normally occupy a nonbonding level in the three-atom molecular orbital in the transition state, but, because of the short distances involved in bonds to hydrogen, there will be considerable Pauli repulsion between the orbitals of R and N, resulting in some antibonding character being conferred on this orbital.

The transition state for hydride transfer should have a short, relatively nonpolarizable bond, whereas that for proton transfer, because of the repulsions caused by the antibonding character of the second filled orbital, should have a longer, more ionic, more polarizable bond. Electron-supplying or -withdrawing substituents on R and N will thus have a larger effect on the force constants for the vibration of the hydrogen atom in the more polarizable bond and should cause variations in the size of the isotope effect for protium-deuterium transfer as compared with hydride-deuteride transfer.

Swain et al. point out that known examples of proton transfer show a considerable variation in the size of the isotope effect from reaction to reaction in agreement with part of the argument above. There seems little direct evidence available, however, to show the effect of substituents in a given reaction where the steric and general mechanistic character of

38. C. G. Swain, R. A. Wiles, and R. F. W. Bader, *J. Am. Chem. Soc.*, **83**, 1945 (1961).

the reactions are the same. They also point out that known examples of hydride-transfer reactions seem to have low isotope effects. However, relatively few clear-cut examples of hydride-transfer reactions have been carefully studied, and in most of these the hydride transfer is only one of several steps in the reaction sequence.

There are two further factors which need to be considered in evaluating the Swain criterion. One is the possibility, discussed earlier, that a nonlinear transition state will provide better geometry for the hydride transfer, unlike the proton-transfer in which extensive studies of hydrogen bonding indicate that the linear arrangement is preferred. A single pair of electrons in a nonlinear bond in the transition state would presumably be more polarizable than those in a linear bond for the same reason that the proton-transfer transition-state bond is polarizable—repulsion between orbitals on the groups R and E.

$$(C_6H_5)_3C^+ + HCO_2^- \rightarrow \left[(C_6H_5)_3\overset{\delta+}{C}\text{---}H\text{---}\overset{\delta-}{C}O_2 \right] \rightarrow (C_6H_5)_3CH + CO_2$$

$$(14)$$

$$(C_6H_5)_3C^+ + H\underset{\underset{CH_3}{|}}{\overset{\overset{CH_3}{|}}{C}}\text{---}OH \rightarrow \left[(C_6H_5)_3\overset{\delta+}{C}\text{---}H\text{---}\underset{\underset{CH_3}{|}}{\overset{\overset{CH_3}{|}}{C}}\overset{\delta+}{=OH} \right] \rightarrow$$

$$(C_6H_5)_3CH \ + \ \underset{\underset{CH_3}{|}}{\overset{\overset{CH_3}{|}}{C}}{=}O \ + \ H^+ \qquad (15)$$

A more serious difficulty is the following: Extensive polarization of bonds *within* the groups R and N and E will occur in the vast majority of proton and hydride transfers that are slow enough to measure by convenient means. That is, R is usually a conjugated system that assists a proton transfer to the nucleophile :N, or a hydride transfer to the electrophile E, by resonance in the transition state. Furthermore, the electrophile E is often a conjugated system in which there is considerable electron polarization toward the "empty" orbital to which the hydride ion will be transferred. Thus, in the hydride-transfer reactions in Eqs. (14) and (15),[39, 40] electron flow within the hydride donor and acceptor may pile up more charge in the three-atom C—H—C orbital of the transition state than would be the case with the idealized nonconjugated

39. R. Stewart, *Can. J. Chem.*, **35**, 766 (1957).
40. P. D. Bartlett and J. D. McCollum, *J. Am. Chem. Soc.*, **78**, 1441 (1956).

system. Similarly, in the proton-abstraction reaction in Eq. (16),[9, 10] the electron flow within the proton donor will reduce the accumulation of charge in the transition state.

$$HO^- + H-\underset{\underset{CH_3}{|}}{\overset{\overset{CH_3}{|}}{C}}-O-NO_2 \rightarrow \left[\overset{\delta-}{HO}---H---\underset{\underset{CH_3}{|}}{\overset{\overset{CH_3}{|}}{C}}=O---\overset{\delta-}{NO_2} \right] \rightarrow$$

$$H_2O + \underset{\underset{CH_3}{|}}{\overset{\overset{CH_3}{|}}{C}}=O + NO_2^- \quad (16)$$

Swain et al. have applied the above criterion of variability of isotope effects to the bromine oxidation of 2-propanol [38] and to the decarboxylation of β-keto acids.[22] They conclude that the former proceeds by a hydride removal from carbon by bromine [Eq. (17)]. They base this

$$Br-Br \quad H-\underset{\underset{CH_3}{|}}{\overset{\overset{CH_3}{|}}{C}}-OH \rightarrow Br^- + HBr + \underset{\underset{CH_3}{|}}{\overset{\overset{CH_3}{|}}{C}}=\overset{+}{O}H \quad (17)$$

conclusion on the fact that 2-propanol exhibits C—H and O—H isotope effects of 2.94 and 1.49, whereas 1-fluoro-2-propanol exhibits C—H and O—H isotope effects of 2.83 and 2.06, the constancy of the value for C—H suggesting a hydride transfer and the variation in the value for O—H, a proton transfer. The fact that the fluoro derivative reacts at only one-thousandth the rate of 2-propanol also suggests a rate-determining hydride loss, since such a strongly electron-withdrawing group should retard such a process.

It should be pointed out that the difference in the rates of these protio and deuterio compounds are not particularly great, nor are the isotope effects themselves nearly as large as those found in most oxidation reactions. Much larger isotope effects and much larger variations with substituents have been observed in the chromic acid and permanganate oxidation of fluoro alcohols. This work is described in Chapters 4 and 5.

CARBON-CARBON BONDS

Carbon-carbon sigma bonds have an extremely low polarizability, and their rupture by oxidizing agents is almost always the result of attack elsewhere in the molecule. In many cases it results from two distinct reactions—an oxidation and a subsequent nonoxidative cleavage of the labile oxidation product.[41] This will occur when such compounds as β-keto acids, *gem*dicarboxylic acids, and α-nitro acids are formed by oxidation of the corresponding alcohols, since decarboxylation occurs readily with compounds of this type.

$$CH_3CHOHCH_2CO_2H \rightarrow CH_3\overset{O}{\overset{\|}{C}}CH_2CO_2H \rightarrow CH_3\overset{O}{\overset{\|}{C}}CH_3 + CO_2$$

$$CH_2OHCH_2CO_2H \rightarrow HO_2CCH_2CO_2H \rightarrow CH_3CO_2H + CO_2$$

$$NO_2CH_2CH_2OH \rightarrow NO_2CH_2CO_2H \rightarrow CH_3NO_2 + CO_2$$

Another form of nonoxidative cleavage is the reverse aldol reaction, and oxidations that produce α-hydroxy aldehydes or ketones, or α,β-unsaturated aldehydes or ketones will be expected, particularly in basic solution, to yield smaller fragments.

$$\underset{R_2\overset{\|}{C}CH_2\overset{\|}{C}HR}{\overset{OH\quad OH}{|\quad\quad|}} \rightarrow \underset{R_2\overset{\|}{C}CH_2\overset{O}{\overset{\|}{C}}R}{\overset{OH\quad O}{|}} \rightarrow R_2C{=}O + CH_3\overset{O}{\overset{\|}{C}}R$$

$$\underset{R_2C{=}CH\overset{\|}{C}HR}{\overset{OH}{|}} \rightarrow R_2C{=}CH\overset{O}{\overset{\|}{C}}R \rightarrow R_2C{=}O + CH_3\overset{O}{\overset{\|}{C}}R$$

A different mechanism is clearly operative in the oxidative decarboxylation of α-hydroxy acids, which is brought about by a variety of reagents.

$$RCHOHCO_2H \xrightarrow{\text{Ox}} RCHO + CO_2$$

This reaction is not a simple analog of the oxidation of β-hydroxy acids, i.e., decarboxylation of the keto acid, since most α-keto acids are not unstable in this way. There are many reaction paths one can write for this reaction, among them the following:

1. Removal of an electron from the carboxylate anion, followed by loss of carbon dioxide and further oxidation [Eq. (18)].

$$RCHOHCO_2^- \overset{e}{\frown} Ox \rightarrow Ox^- + RCHOHCO_2\cdot \xrightarrow{-CO_2}$$

$$\qquad\qquad RC\underset{\bullet}{H}OH \xrightarrow{-e} RCHO + H^+ \quad (18)$$

41. M. M. Shemyakin and L. A. Shchukina, *Quart. Revs. (London)*, **1956**, 261.

2. Hydride removal from the hydroxyl group of the anion, aided by participation of neighboring carboxylate [Eq. (19)].

$$
\underset{\substack{| \\ \text{RCH—CO}_2^-}}{\overset{\substack{\text{Ox} \\ \text{O} \overset{\curvearrowleft}{-}\text{H}}}{}} \rightarrow \text{RCHO} + \text{HOx}^- + \text{CO}_2 \tag{19}
$$

3. Decomposition of a cyclic metal complex of the hydroxy acid [Eq. (20)].

$$
\begin{array}{c}
\text{M} \\
\text{O} \diagup \quad \diagdown \text{O} \\
| \qquad\qquad | \\
\text{RCH} \text{——} \text{C}{=}\text{O}
\end{array} \rightarrow \text{RCHO} + \text{CO}_2 + \text{M} \tag{20}
$$

Among the reagents that accomplish oxidative decarboxylation are lead tetra-acetate,[42] manganese dioxide,[43] silver benzoate–iodine,[44] sodium hypochlorite,[45] and electrolytic oxidation.[46] Little information on mechanism is available, but it seems reasonable to assume that the electrolytic oxidation (page 128) proceeds by path 1. On the other hand, Fenton's reagent,[47] peroxide and ferrous ion, oxidizes lactic acid to pyruvic acid, not to acetaldehyde and carbon dioxide. Hydroxyl radicals, the principal oxidants in Fenton's reagent,[48] presumably prefer to abstract hydrogens from the carbinol group in this case.[49]

$$
\text{CH}_3\text{CHOHCO}_2\text{H} \xrightarrow{\text{HO·}} \overset{\overset{\text{O}}{\|}}{\text{CH}_3\text{CCO}_2\text{H}}
$$

42. H. Oeda, *Bull. Chem. Soc. Japan*, **9**, 8 (1934).
43. J. Liebig, *Ann.*, **113**, 1 (1860).
44. P. S. Raman, *Current Sci. (India)*, **27**, 22 (1958).
45. R. L. Whistler and K. Yagi, *J. Org. Chem.*, **26**, 1050 (1961).
46. C. Neuberg, L. Scott, and S. Lachmann, *Biochem. Z.*, **24**, 152 (1910).
47. H. J. H. Fenton and H. O. Jones, *J. Chem. Soc.*, **77**, 69 (1900).
48. For an account of the chemistry of Fenton's reagent, see W. A. Waters, *Chemistry of Free Radicals*, Oxford, London, 1948, p. 247, and J. Weiss, *Advances in Catalysis*, **4**, 343 (1952).
49. Ruff's method for degrading aldonic acids to aldoses with one less carbon makes use of hydrogen peroxide and *ferric* ion and is an oxidative decarboxylation. See H. G. Fletcher, Jr., H. W. Diehl, and C. S. Hudson, *J. Am. Chem. Soc.*, **72**, 4546 (1950), and references therein.

Certain dicarboxylic acids also undergo oxidative decarboxylation. Ferricyanide, which is normally a 1-equivalent electron–transfer reagent (page 84), causes the aromatizations shown in Eqs. (21) and (22),[50, 51] probably by mechanisms analogous to that of the anodic oxidation of α-hydroxy acids, referred to above.

$$\text{(structure)} \xrightarrow[(-4e)]{Fe(CN)_6{}^{3-}} \text{(structure)} + 2CO_2 + 2H^+ \qquad (21)$$

$$\text{(structure)} \xrightarrow[(-2e)]{Fe(CN)_6{}^{3-}} \text{(structure)} + CO_2 + H^+ \qquad (22)$$

The mechanism of the process in Eq. (23)[52, 53] is probably different, however, since lead tetraacetate is known to prefer other reaction paths, notably cyclic ones (page 99).

$$\text{(structure)}\!-\!\begin{array}{l}CO_2H\\CO_2H\end{array} \xrightarrow[\text{or Pb(OAc)}_4]{PbO_2} \text{(structure)} + 2CO_2 \qquad (23)$$

Clearly, much more information on the mechanism of oxidative decarboxylation reactions is required.[54, 55]

50. T. W. Campbell and R. N. McDonald, *J. Org. Chem.*, **24**, 730 (1959).
51. J. F. Walker and N. D. Scott, *J. Am. Chem. Soc.*, **60**, 951 (1938).
52. W. von E. Doering, M. Farber, and A. Sayigh, *J. Am. Chem. Soc.*, **74**, 4370 (1952).
53. C. A. Grob, M. Ohta, and A. Weiss, *Angew. Chem.*, **70**, 343 (1958); C. A. Grob, M. Ohta, E. Renk, and A. Weiss, *Helv. Chim. Acta*, **41**, 1191 (1958).
54. Biochemical oxidative decarboxylations have been more intensively studied; see, for example, page 157.
55. Reactions that are formally oxidative decarboxylations, and whose mechanisms have all been studied, are the Hunsdiecker reaction,[56] the Hofmann hypohalite reaction,[57] and the bromination of a parahydroxybenzoic acid.[58]
56. R. G. Johnson and R. K. Ingham, *Chem. Revs.*, **56**, 219 (1956).
57. C. R. Hauser and S. W. Kantor, *J. Am. Chem. Soc.*, **72**, 4284 (1950).
58. E. Grovenstein, Jr., and G. A. Ropp, *J. Am. Chem. Soc.*, **78**, 2560 (1956), and references therein.

The Hooker oxidation is an interesting reaction [Eq. (24)] in which several processes combine to produce an unusual skeletal change.

$$Z\text{-naphthoquinone with -OH, -CH}_2R \xrightarrow[\text{OH}^-]{\text{MnO}_4^-} Z\text{-naphthoquinone with -R, -OH} + CO_2 \qquad (24)$$

Fieser and Fieser[59] and Shemyakin et al.[60] have elucidated the reaction mechanism, which can be written as in Eq. (25).

$$\text{[reaction scheme]} \qquad (25)$$

Bonds between partially oxidized carbon atoms are particularly susceptible to oxidative cleavage. A variety of both 1- and 2-equivalent reagents (e.g., periodic acid, permanganate, manganese pyrophosphate) cleave pinacol to acetone, usually via cyclic intermediates (see Chapter 7).

The facile cleavage of carbon-carbon bonds in 1,2-dicarbonyl compounds is well known. Peracids convert α-diketones, o-quinones and α-ketoesters to anhydrides in nonaqueous solution, whereas aqueous conditions normally yield the acids.

$$\underset{\text{RC—C—OEt}}{\overset{\text{O O}}{\|\ \|}} \xrightarrow{\text{RCO}_3\text{H}} \underset{\text{RC—O—COEt}}{\overset{\text{O O}}{\|\ \ \ \|}}$$

59. L. F. Fieser and M. Fieser, J. Am. Chem. Soc., 70, 3215 (1948).
60. L. A. Shchukina, A. P. Kondratieva, and M. M. Shemyakin, Zhur. obshchei. Khim., 18, 1945 (1948).

Ketones that can enolize are subject to degradation by powerful oxidants, and the mechanism is presumably similar to the cleavage of olefins.

Enolization is not involved in the Baeyer-Villiger oxidation of ketones, however. In this reaction, peracids, such as performic acid, Caro's acid (H_2SO_5), etc., convert aromatic ketones to esters. The reaction is accelerated by polar solvents, the carbonyl oxygen in the ketone becomes the carbonyl oxygen in the ester, and the aryl group migrates (as in most 1,2-shifts) in preference to the alkyl group. The mechanism is thus probably that shown in Eq. (26).[61-63]

$$
\underset{\text{ArCCH}_3}{\overset{O}{\parallel}} \xrightarrow{\text{RCO}_3\text{H}} \underset{\substack{| \\ \text{O}_3\text{CR}}}{\overset{\text{OH}}{\underset{|}{\text{ArCCH}_3}}} \rightarrow \left[\underset{\text{O}}{\overset{\text{OH}}{\text{Ar}\cdots\text{C—CH}_3}} \right] \rightarrow \underset{\text{ArOCCH}_3}{\overset{O}{\parallel}} + \text{H}^+ + \text{RCO}_2^-
$$

$$(26)$$

The Dakin reaction,[64] which converts ortho and para hydroxy and amino aldehydes and ketones to the corresponding phenols, presumably follows a similar course [Eq. (27)]. Most aliphatic ketones give very poor yields of esters in this reaction, polymeric peroxides being produced instead.

$$(27)$$

Carbon-carbon double bonds are readily cleaved by powerful oxidants, such as permanganate. The action of ozone is well known and proceeds through the ozonide $\overset{O—O}{\underset{O}{\diagup C \diagdown\diagup C\diagdown}}$ produced, it is believed, by

61. W. von E. Doering and E. Dorfman, *J. Am. Chem. Soc.*, **75**, 5595 (1953).
62. R. Criegee, *Ann.*, **560**, 127 (1948).
63. S. L. Friess, *J. Am. Chem. Soc.*, **71**, 2571 (1949).
64. H. D. Dakin, in *Organic Syntheses* Coll. vol. I, Wiley, New York, 1941, p. 149.

rearrangement of the unstable primary ozonide $\overset{\diagdown}{C}\overset{O_3}{-}\overset{\diagup}{C}$. The various structures suggested for the primary ozonide are discussed by Bailey.[65]

On the other hand, carbon-carbon triple bonds are much more inert to the action of most oxidants, just as they are to the action of electrophiles in general. The preservation of the triple bond in the following reaction illustrates this.[66]

$$HC\equiv C(CH_2)_7CH=C(C_6H_5)_2 \xrightarrow[\text{aq.HOAc}]{Cr^{VI}} HC\equiv C(CH_2)_7CO_2H$$

65. P. S. Bailey, *Chem. Revs.*, **58**, 925 (1958).
66. H. K. Black and B. C. L. Weedon, *J. Chem. Soc.*, **1953,** 1785.

chapter four | Chromic Acid Oxidations

Chromic acid is an extremely important oxidant in both organic and inorganic chemistry. It has occupied an equally important position in the study of oxidation mechanisms following the pioneer work of Westheimer in the 1940s. Like permanganate ion, to be discussed in the following chapter, chromic acid is a powerful oxidant whose activity is a function of the acidity of the medium. Unlike permanganate, however, its ability to oxidize organic compounds virtually vanishes in basic solution. There are a number of other points of difference between manganese(VII) and chromium(VI) that complicate the study of the oxidation mechanisms of the latter. These are the equilibrium between chromate and bichromate, the ability of chromium(VI) to bond or coordinate with other ions in solution, and the participation of intermediate chromium(IV) and chromium(V) species in the oxidations. These points will be discussed in later sections. Chromic acid does possess one advantage over permanganate in terms of both synthetic uses and mechanistic studies—it and its derivatives are more stable than permanganate in nonaqueous media.

OXIDATION STATES OF CHROMIUM

Oxidation states from $+2$ to $+6$ are known for chromium, and in addition chromium(VI) can form peroxy compounds. Chromium(VI) is normally reduced to chromium(III) in a redox reaction, since the intermediate chromium(V) and chromium(IV) species are unstable under ordinary conditions, and since chromium(II) is an excellent reducing agent.

In anhydrous acetic acid or in acetic anhydride, incomplete reduction of chromium(VI) is sometimes observed even in the presence of a large excess of reducing agent. Brown insoluble complexes of chromium(III), chromium(VI), and acetate are known to be formed in these cases.[1]

Chromium(V) can exist in strongly basic solution, but it disproportionates under ordinary conditions. Disproportionation is not the sole fate of chromium(V) or chromium(IV) ions formed as intermediates in redox reactions, however. The work of Westheimer et al.[2,3] has demonstrated clearly that these ions participate in the oxidation of organic substrates. Indeed, the intermediate chromium species appear to be much more vigorous oxidizing agents than chromium(VI). They may be responsible, too, for the uptake of oxygen that is sometimes observed during chromium(VI) oxidations.

Chromium (VI)

The equilibrium between acid chromate and bichromate is a function of concentration. In very dilute solution, most of the chromium(VI) is in the monomer form both in water and in 91 per cent acetic acid.[4,5]

$$2HCrO_4^- \rightleftharpoons Cr_2O_7^= + H_2O$$

The acid chromate ion, $HCrO_4^-$ does not lose its proton until the pH is raised to about 7;[6,7] it gains a second proton in the H_- range of -1 to -3, depending on the particular acid solution used.[8,9]

By examining the effect of changing concentration on the reaction rate, Novick and Westheimer were able to show that the oxidation of isopropyl alcohol by chromium(VI) involved a monomeric, not a dimeric, chromium species. In strongly acid solution, higher polymers of chromium(VI) have been detected.[10]

1. R. Slack and W. A. Waters, *J. Chem. Soc.*, **1949**, 599.
2. F. H. Westheimer, *Chem. Revs.*, **45**, 419 (1949).
3. W. Watanabe and F. H. Westheimer, *J. Chem. Phys.*, **17**, 61 (1949).
4. J. Y. Tong and E. L. King, *J. Am. Chem. Soc.*, **75**, 6180 (1953).
5. K. B. Wiberg and T. Mill, *J. Am. Chem. Soc.*, **80**, 3022 (1958).
6. J. R. Howard, V. S. K. Nair, and G. H. Nancollas, *Trans. Faraday Soc.*, **54**, 1034 (1958).
7. J. D. Neuss and W. Riemann, *J. Am. Chem. Soc.*, **56**, 2238 (1934).
8. N. Bailey, A. Carrington, K. A. K. Lott, and M. C. R. Symons, *J. Chem. Soc.*, **1960**, 290.
9. R. Stewart and D. G. Lee, unpublished results.
10. E. Pungor and J. Trompler, *J. Inorg. & Nuclear Chem.*, **5**, 123 (1957).

Induced Oxidation

In dilute acid solution, H_2CrO_4 does not oxidize Mn^{++} to MnO_2, and, indeed, above $pH \approx 0$ the reaction is thermodynamically un-favorable. However, in the presence of sufficient manganous ion (or cerous ion), the rate at which chromic acid is reduced to chromium(III) by isopropyl alcohol is decreased by about 50 per cent. The manganous ion is converted to MnO_2, and the oxidants that accomplish this must be chromium(V) or chromium(IV) formed by the initial chromium(VI)-alcohol reaction. Chromium(II) is an unlikely intermediate because of its strong reducing action on water.

$$Cr^{VI} + Mn^{++} \rightarrow \text{no reaction}$$

$$2Cr^{VI} + 3(CH_3)_2CHOH \rightarrow 2Cr^{III} + 3(CH_3)_2C{=}O$$

$$2Cr^{VI} + 2(CH_3)_2CHOH + Mn^{++} \rightarrow 2Cr^{III} + 2(CH_3)_2C{=}O + MnO_2$$

The induction factor for the third reaction above is $\frac{1}{2}$; this is the ratio of the number of moles of MnO_2 to acetone formed in the reaction. In reality, the induction factor approaches $\frac{1}{2}$ only as the Mn^{++} concentration is made large, since the very reactive chromium(IV) or chromium(V) ions will react with alcohol (or, in some cases, the solvent) if manganous ions are scarce or absent.

Assuming chromium(IV) is the only reactive chromium inter-mediate, the reaction in the presence of manganous ion can be written as follows:

$$HCrO_4^- + (CH_3)_2CHOH \rightarrow (CH_3)_2C{=}O + Cr^{IV}$$

$$Cr^{IV} + Mn^{++} \rightarrow Cr^{III} + Mn^{III}$$

$$2Mn^{III} \rightarrow MnO_2 + Mn^{++}$$

The lower rate of reduction of chromium(VI) in the presence of added Mn^{++} appears at first glance to be anomalous, since the Mn^{++} is itself an efficient reducing agent that effects rapid reduction of the intermediate chromium species formed in the initial reaction with alcohol. In the absence of manganous ion, however, the chromium(IV) acts as a *reducing* agent and reacts with a second molecule of chromium(VI) to form two of chromium(V), which subsequently oxidize two more molecules of alcohol.

Westheimer, Wiberg, and others have examined the various ways in which chromium(V) and chromium(IV) can intervene in the oxidation of organic substrates.[3, 11] If all the reactions of the organic substrate with

11. K. B. Wiberg and W. H. Richardson, *J. Am. Chem. Soc.*, **84**, 2800 (1962).

chromium ions are 2-equivalent reactions [as the initial step of the chromium(VI)-alcohol reaction almost certainly is[3]], then the following sequence occurs:

$$ZH_2 + Cr^{VI} \rightarrow Z + Cr^{IV} + 2H^+$$
$$Cr^{IV} + Cr^{VI} \rightarrow 2Cr^V$$
$$2ZH_2 + 2Cr^V \rightarrow 2Z + 2Cr^{III} + 4H^+$$

If the initial reaction is a 1-equivalent step, the following is the most likely sequence. [The initial steps in some chromium(VI)-hydrocarbon reactions appear to be 1-equivalent reactions.[12]]

$$ZH_2 + Cr^{VI} \rightarrow ZH\cdot + Cr^V + H^+$$
$$ZH\cdot + Cr^{VI} \rightarrow Z + Cr^V + H^+$$
$$2ZH_2 + 2Cr^V \rightarrow 2Z + 2Cr^{III} + 4H^+$$

If the initial reaction between chromium(VI) and the organic compound is a 2-equivalent step, but the subsequent reaction of chromium(IV) is a 1-equivalent oxidation of the organic compound, then the following sequence occurs:

$$ZH_2 + Cr^{VI} \rightarrow Z + Cr^{IV} + 2H^+$$
$$ZH_2 + Cr^{IV} \rightarrow ZH\cdot + Cr^{III} + H^+$$
$$ZH\cdot + Cr^{VI} \rightarrow Z + Cr^V + H^+$$
$$ZH_2 + Cr^V \rightarrow Z + Cr^{III} + 2H^+$$

The important role of chromium(V) and chromium(IV) as oxidants can be seen by examining the three sets of possible reactions above. In the first two, chromium(VI) accounts for only one-third of the total oxidation, and chromium(V) for two-thirds. In the third set, the chromium(VI) accounts for half the oxidizing equivalents, and chromium(IV) and (V) for the other half.

In the above reaction sequences, disproportionation as the fate of the intermediate chromium species has been ignored, but under highly dilute reaction conditions it may become important.

Wiberg and Richardson[11] have been able to learn something of the reactivity of chromium(IV) and (V) toward organic substrates by the use of competition experiments, using chromium(VI) to oxidize mixtures of aromatic aldehydes. Thus, if the relative reactivities of a pair of aldehydes

12. K. B. Wiberg and R. J. Evans, *Tetrahedron*, **8**, 313 (1960).

toward the chromium intermediate differs from their relative reactivities toward chromium(VI), this can be detected.

Since the intermediates are more vigorous oxidants than chromium(VI), one might expect that less discrimination would exist in their choice of substrates. Wiberg and Richardson have shown that, if only chromium(VI) and (V) are involved in the oxidation of a series of aromatic aldehydes, then the rho value for chromium(V) is smaller [0.45, compared with 0.77 for chromium(VI)], indicating less discrimination by the more active oxidant. If both chromium(IV) and (V) take part in the oxidation of the aldehydes, the analysis of the results is more difficult, but it indicates a higher positive rho for the chromium(V) oxidation. The mechanism of the aldehyde oxidations is considered in some detail in a later section.

ALCOHOLS

The results of the studies by Westheimer and his group on the oxidation of isopropyl alcohol by chromic acid can be summarized as follows: (1) The reaction is acid-catalyzed, the rate being dependent on the first (or in some cases a higher) power of the hydrogen-ion (or h_0) concentration; (2) the reaction is much faster in acetic acid solution than in mineral acids of the same H_0 value; (3) the transition state contains a monochromium, not a dichromium, species; (4) there is a kinetic isotope effect of 6.6 at 25° for the oxidation of $(CH_3)_2CDOH$; and (5) added manganous ion reduces the rate of reduction of the chromium(VI) by a factor of 2.

All these facts can be accommodated by the mechanism in Eqs. (1), in which a chromate ester decomposes by proton loss to any available base with elimination of a chromium(IV) ion.

$$(CH_3)_2CHOH + HCrO_4^- + 2H^+ \rightarrow (CH_3)_2CHOCrO_3H_2^+ + H_2O$$

$$\begin{array}{c} H_3C \\ \diagdown \\ C \diagdown O-CrO_3H_2^+ \\ H_3C \diagup \diagdown H \\ \curvearrowright :B \end{array} \longrightarrow \begin{array}{c} H_3C \\ \diagdown \\ C{=}O + BH^+ + H_2CrO_3(Cr^{IV}) \\ H_3C \diagup \end{array}$$

followed by

$$Cr^{IV} + Cr^{VI} \xrightarrow{fast} 2Cr^V \qquad (1)$$

$$2Cr^V + 2(CH_3)_2CHOH \xrightarrow{fast} 2Cr^{III} + 2(CH_3)_2C{=}O + 4H^+$$

or by

$$Cr^{IV} + Mn^{II} \xrightarrow{\text{fast}} Cr^{III} + Mn^{III}$$

$$Cr^{IV} + Mn^{III} \xrightarrow{\text{fast}} Cr^{III} + MnO_2$$

The heterolytic scission of the chromium-oxygen bond in the ester will obviously be aided by an accumulation of positive charge on the chromium atom, hence the catalysis by protons. The increased rate in acetic acid might reflect a medium shift in the equilibrium toward the ester as a result of the lower dielectric constant of the medium, or it might result from formation of a more reactive acetyl chromate ester.

The fact that the ester, isopropyl chromate, can be prepared and its decomposition in benzene is accelerated by pyridine[13] shows that the Eq. (1) mechanism (an E_2 elimination analogous to nitrate-ester decomposition, page 16) is a most reasonable one but does not prove that the ester is an intermediate in the oxidation under ordinary conditions.

The participation of an external base in the decomposition of the ester has proved difficult to detect. The reaction rates are extremely slow in the dilute aqueous region where general acid catalysis might be detected. The small effect of added pyridine on the reaction rate in acid solution was shown not to be the result of participation by this base in the rate-controlling step.

Despite general acceptance of the Westheimer bimolecular ester-decomposition mechanism for the chromic acid oxidation of alcohols, Roček,[14] in 1958, reopened the case. His objections were based principally on three arguments. First, he pointed out that evidence indicating the participation of external base in the reaction was at best inconclusive. Secondly, he suggested that the reaction should not follow the h_0 function (as it does between 5 and 70 per cent sulfuric acid) if water, which is the only likely base present, participates. This argument was based on the Zucker-Hammett hypothesis that such a reaction should follow the oxonium-ion concentration instead. The Zucker-Hammett hypothesis is now suspect, but in any case it was shown by Graham and Westheimer[15] that this argument is invalid, since the mole of water produced in the preequilibrium step cancels out the mole of water used as reactant in the second step. The rate equations for the Westheimer mechanism and the

13. A. Leo and F. H. Westheimer, *J. Am. Chem. Soc.*, **74**, 4383 (1952).
14. J. Roček and J. Krupička, *Collection Czechoslov. Chem. Commun.*, **23**, 2068 (1958).
15. G. T. E. Graham and F. H. Westheimer, *J. Am. Chem. Soc.*, **80**, 3030 (1958).

mechanism suggested by Roček (see below) were, in fact, identical, and hence the same acidity function will govern both reactions. The rate law in each case reduces to

$$v = [R_2CHOH][H_2CrO_4]h_0$$

In some less acidic systems, the transition-state composition has one less proton. Thus, in aqueous acetic acid, the rate law becomes $v = [R_2CHOH][HCrO_4^-]h_0$.[16] (The appropriate acidity function in this case is actually h_-, but this function has not been determined for acetic acid.)

The third objection to the ester mechanism is the effect of substituents on the oxidation of phenyl methyl carbinols.

The Hammett rho value for this reaction was shown to be fairly large and negative ($\rho = -1.01$ when $R = CH_3$ and -1.01 when $R = CF_3$).[9,17] The modified rho, which correlates certain reactions of aliphatic compounds,[18] is also negative for the chromium(VI) oxidation of aliphatic alcohols, $\rho^* = -1.06$ for primary alcohols[19] and -1.11 for secondary alcohols.[9] The rate-controlling decomposition of the chromate ester by proton removal might be expected to be positive; i.e., electron-withdrawing groups, such as nitro, should facilitate the loss of a proton from the 1-carbon more than they discourage the loss of an electron pair from the more remote oxygen-chromium bond.[20] The base-catalyzed decomposition of the analogous nitrate ester has a large positive rho value, $\rho = +3.6$. It can be argued that the rho for the preequilibrium step is more than sufficient to overcome the rho of the rate-controlling step, but measurements of alcohol-chromium(VI) equilibria indicate that the rho of these reactions is less than 1.

16. M. Cohen and F. H. Westheimer, *J. Am. Chem. Soc.*, **74**, 4387 (1952).
17. H. Kwart and P. S. Francis, *J. Am. Chem. Soc.*, **77**, 4907 (1955).
18. R. W. Taft, Jr., in M. S. Newman (ed.), *Steric Effects in Organic Chemistry*, Wiley, New York, 1956.
19. J. Roček, *Collection Czechoslov. Chem. Commun.*, **25**, 1052 (1960).
20. If the chromate-ester decomposition has some E_1 character (carbon-hydrogen bond rupture less advanced than chromium-oxygen bond rupture in the transition state), then the rho value could conceivably be negative. The large C—D isotope effects found in the Cr^{VI}-alcohol reactions indicate, however, that carbon-hydrogen bond rupture is well advanced in the transition state.

Roček and Krupička suggested that a direct hydride transfer from alcohol to chromic acid or to its conjugate acid, chromic acidium ion, would be a more reasonable reaction path.[14, 21] A simple hydride transfer from C—H to the chromium species is unsatisfactory, however, since it would lead one to predict that ethers should be easily oxidized. Diisopropyl ether is, in fact, oxidized at only one fifteenth-hundredth the rate of isopropyl alcohol.[22] They suggested that a simultaneous proton loss from the hydroxyl group occurred as the carbon-hydrogen bond was cleaved [Eq. (2)]. The chromium(IV) species could then decompose as before.

$$\begin{array}{ccc}
H_3C & O\!-\!H & HO \quad OH \\
C & & Cr \\
H_3C & H & O \quad OH
\end{array} \rightarrow (CH_3)_2C\!=\!O + H_5CrO_4^+ \qquad (2)$$

The solvent isotope effect, observed when D_2O is used, effectively eliminates this mechanism, however. The rate of oxidation of isopropyl alcohol in D_2O is 2.4 times *faster* than the reaction in H_2O under conditions in which the kinetic dependence on acid concentration was of the first order.[22] This results from the greater acidity of D_3O^+ compared with H_3O^+ and the consequent larger concentration of the reactive conjugate acid. The latter is the protonated chromate ester in the Westheimer mechanism and the chromic acidium ion in the Roček mechanism. In the latter mechanism, however, an oxygen-hydrogen bond is broken in the rate-controlling step, and this would produce a primary kinetic isotope effect that should at least cancel the solvent isotope effect. (The rapid exchange of hydroxyl protons with the solvent produces hydroxyl groups that are deuterated.)

The oxygen-hydrogen bond of the alcohol can neither be intact in the transition state [because of the relative inertness of ethers to chromium(VI)] nor be broken in the transition state (because of the positive, solvent isotope effect). It is reasonable to conclude, then, that the ester is an intermediate in the oxidation path.[23] If one considers a unimolecular

21. A mechanism of this type had originally been advanced by Westheimer and Novick early in the investigation of the Cr^{VI}-alcohol reaction. [F. H. Westheimer and A. Novick, *J. Chem. Phys.*, **11**, 506 (1943).]
22. R. Brownell, A. Leo, Y. W. Chang, and F. H. Westheimer, *J. Am. Chem. Soc.*, **82**, 406 (1960).
23. Further support for an ester mechanism comes from the fact that an isotope effect of 1.0 has been found for the oxidation of a highly hindered secondary alcohol $3\beta,28$-diacetoxy-6β-hydroxy-18β-12-oleanen, in 80 per cent acetic acid; in less acidic solution where the reaction is slower, an isotope effect of 2.0 was found. Presumably, in the former case, ester

decomposition mechanism for the chromate ester, the rate-controlling step in Eq. (3) is possible.

Kwart and Francis have written a transition state similar to (I) in Eq. (3) but with the hydrogen on carbon transferred to the oxygen on chromium as a proton.[24, 25] The difficulty in assigning direction to

$$
\begin{array}{c}
\text{H}_3\text{C} \\
 \\
\text{H}_3\text{C}
\end{array}
\!\!\!\!\!
\underset{\text{H}\quad\text{O}}{\overset{\text{O}}{\text{C}}}
\!\!\!\!\!
\text{CrO}_2\text{H}_2^+ \rightarrow
\left[
\begin{array}{c}
\text{H}_3\text{C} \\
 \\
\text{H}_3\text{C}
\end{array}
\!\!\!\!\!
\underset{\text{H---O}}{\overset{\text{O}}{\text{C}}}
\!\!\!\!\!
\text{CrO}_2\text{H}_2^+
\right] \rightarrow
$$

$$
\begin{array}{c}
\text{H}_3\text{C} \\
 \\
\text{H}_3\text{C}
\end{array}
\!\!\!\!\!
\text{C}=\text{O} + \text{H}_3\text{CrO}_3^+ \tag{3}
$$

(I)

electron flow in cyclic transition states has been commented on earlier. However, if the hydrogen in the C—H bond, above, is transferred to the oxygen of the chromate as a proton, the reaction path would appear to have little to recommend it in comparison with the bimolecular mechanism in which the proton is transferred to a molecule of water. The latter should certainly be a stronger base than an oxygen atom in the chromate.

$$
\begin{array}{c}
\!\!\!\!\! \\
\text{C} \\
\!\!\!\!\!
\end{array}
\!\!\!\!\!
\underset{\text{H}\quad\text{O}}{\overset{\text{O}}{}}
\!\!\!\!\!
\text{Cr} \rightarrow
\left[
\begin{array}{c}
\!\!\!\!\! \\
\text{C} \\
\!\!\!\!\!
\end{array}
\!\!\!\!\!
\underset{\text{H}\quad\text{O}}{\overset{\text{O}}{}}
\!\!\!\!\!
\text{Cr}
\right] \rightarrow
\!\!\!\!\!
\text{C}=\text{O} +
\underset{\text{HO}}{}
:\text{Cr} \tag{4}
$$

(II)

If the cyclic transition state is correct, it seems reasonable to assume that the transfer of electrons toward the chromium would also occur through the orbitals linking the carbon, hydrogen, and oxygen atoms in the transition state. Simple chemical bond structures for such a reaction path are shown in Eq. (4), in which each dotted arrow indicates the relocation of approximately one electron unit. In the extreme case of

formation became rate-controlling. [J. Roček, F. H. Westheimer, A. Eschenmoser, L. Moldoványi, and J. Schreiber, *Helv. Chim. Acta*, **45**, 2554 (1962). This paper contains a valuable discussion of the structural factors that affect the chromium(VI)-alcohol reaction. A mechanism involving a cyclic transition state (see above) is also considered.]

24. H. Kwart and P. S. Francis, *J. Am. Chem. Soc.*, **81**, 2116 (1959).
25. H. Kwart, *Suomen Kemistilehti*, **A34**, 173 (1961).

proton or hydride transfer (if these terms have any significance in this context), three of the dotted lines would represent transfer of two electrons; and the other three, the transfer of none. The structures (I) and (II) in Eqs. (3) and (4) are different ways of depicting the same transition state. The developing carbonyl group will be stabilized by electron-donating groups, and the accelerating effects of such groups in the aryl carbinol series has been mentioned earlier.[26]

If one accepts the above argument, the accelerating effect of electron-donating groups must be attributed to their ability to supply charge to an electron-deficient transition state.

Although the unimolecular chromate–ester mechanism discussed above appears to be satisfactory, there are two further sets of data, which have been accumulated about the reaction, that must be considered. These are (1) the variation of the deuterium-isotope effect for the oxidation of $>$CDOH with the structure of the attached groups; and (2) the variation of the reaction rate with acidity of the medium. The theoretical basis of each of these subjects—the magnitude of isotope effects and the correlation of rates with acidities—can hardly be considered as being firmly established at present. Nonetheless, it is worth analyzing the information available in terms of mechanism. It should be pointed out that the three mechanisms discussed earlier—the decomposition of the chromate ester by bimolecular and by unimolecular steps and the bimolecular hydride mechanism—give identical rate laws.[27]

Isotope Effects

A "normal" isotope effect of 7:1 at room temperature is observed for the oxidation of $(CH_3)CDOH$ by chromic acid, showing that the rate-controlling step involves the rupture of the carbon-hydrogen bond.[13, 28] Rather wide variations in the size of the isotope effect have been observed when the methyls are substituted in various ways.

26. Kwart believes that the carbonyl character cannot be highly developed in the transition state because of the small rate difference in the chromium(VI) oxidation of pairs of alcohols that give ketones of widely differing carbonyl stability, e. g., cyclohexanone vs. cyclopentanone or 7-ketonorbornane. (Refs. 25 and 37.)
27. Strictly speaking, the rate laws for the bimolecular ester and bimolecular hydride mechanisms become identical only if water is the only base available to decompose the ester; further, the rate law for the unimolecular ester mechanism becomes identical to these only if the water activity is the same over the region studied.
28. F. H. Westheimer and N. Nicolaides, *J. Am. Chem. Soc.*, **71**, 25 (1949). See also L. Kaplan, *J. Am. Chem. Soc.*, **77**, 5469 (1955).

Introduction of alkyl groups or aryl groups, such as p-anisyl, increases the rate of oxidation largely because of the electron-donating character of these groups. Smaller isotope effects, between 4:1 and 6:1, are observed.[25] Conversely, introduction of strongly electron-attracting groups, such as nitrophenyl or fluoromethyl, cause the rate to drop and the isotope effect to rise to values as high as 13:1 in the case of 3,5-dinitrophenyltrifluoromethyl carbinol.[9] A rough inverse relation appears to exist between the logarithm of the oxidation rate and the isotope effect. A similar effect of strongly electron-withdrawing groups on the isotope effect in the permanganate oxidation of alcohols is discussed in Chapter 5.

Attempts have been made to correlate the size of an isotope effect with the degree of bond breaking in the transition state.[29-31] The difficulties in such a scheme are magnified by the very large isotope effects observed in some oxidation reactions. Either alterations in the bending modes in the transition state or proton tunneling must be invoked to account for them. It may be significant that large isotope effects (> 10 at room temperature) are observed chiefly in oxidation reactions in which hydrogen-atom transfer and hydride-ion transfer become possible reaction paths.

Acid Dependence

The rate of the chromium(VI)-alcohol reaction rises sharply with increasing acidity of the medium until a maximum rate is reached in fairly concentrated acid. This leveling off in rate occurs at about 60 to 80 per cent sulfuric acid, depending on the structure of the alcohol, and results either from protonation of the alcohol or, more likely, from complete protonation of the chromate ester.

At lower acidities, linear relations between the logarithm of the rate and the acidity function H_0 are found. In aqueous acetic acid containing added mineral acid and in certain concentration ranges of aqueous mineral acids, a unit slope is obtained indicating a first-order dependency on the hydrogen ion or, more precisely, h_0 concentration. This is in accordance with the requirement of the transition state for one proton in addition to chromium(VI) and alcohol. Since neutral chromic acid appears to be the preponderant chromium(VI) species at these acidities, the reaction path can be written as follows, assuming the ester is an intermediate in the oxidation:

$$H_2CrO_4 + ROH + H^+ \rightleftharpoons ROCrO_3H_2^+ + H_2O \rightarrow \text{products}$$

29. F. H. Westheimer, *Chem. Revs.*, **61**, 265 (1961).
30. R. P. Bell, *Proton in Chemistry*, Cornell, Ithaca, N.Y., 1959.
31. E. R. Thornton, *J. Org. Chem.*, **27**, 1943 (1962).

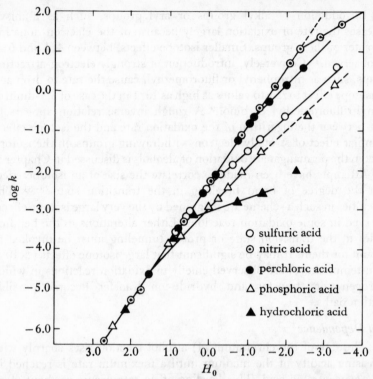

Figure 1 *The variation of the rate of chromic acid oxidation of isopropyl alcohol with acidity for various mineral acids.*

Anomalies appear, however, when the effect of varying the mineral acid is examined. Figure 1 shows the variation of rate with acidity for various mineral acids,[9] and the profound effect of the various acid anions on the oxidation rate is apparent.[32] A similar effect is observed when the ionization constant of chromic acid, H_2CrO_4, is measured spectrophotometrically in different media.[9] The apparent pK, based on conventional acidity functions, such as H_0, H_-, or $H_R(J_0)$, varies with the particular acid used. The apparent pK is in most cases not far from the acidity at which the changes of slope occur in Figure 1. Apparently the chromium(VI) species in acidic solution can include the anion of the mineral acid, and Cohen and Westheimer observed a decrease in rate and an alteration in the chromium(VI) spectrum when hydrochloric acid was

32. This assumes that H_0 is an appropriate function to plot against log k.

used instead of sulfuric acid.[16, 33] They attributed it to the formation of the weaker oxidant $ClCrO_3^-$ replacing $HCrO_4^-$ in solution.

$$HCrO_4^- + H^+ + Cl^- \rightleftharpoons ClCrO_3^- + H_2O$$

Apparently, this is a general phenomenon, and it may well be that the formation of the reactive chromium(VI) ester should be written as follows:

$$HCrO_4^- + 2H^+ + A^- \rightleftharpoons HCrO_3A + H_2O$$

$$HCrO_3A + ROH + H^+ \rightleftharpoons ROCrO_2AH^+ + H_2O$$

$$ROCrO_2AH^+ \rightarrow products$$

In the region below the apparent pK, the rate is independent of the particular strong acid that is used. Acetic acid as solvent, rather than water, causes large increases in rate, possibly because of a solvent effect and possibly because of a specific effect when A = acetyl in the above equations.

The fractional dependence of the rate on the hydrogen-ion concentration in dilute aqueous acids is rather strange. It is just possible that the slope of about 1.5 in the plot of log k against H_0 is caused by a fortuitous combination of circumstances, e.g., contributions from terms that are first and second order in H^+ (corresponding to reaction of the esters $ROCrO_3H$ and $ROCrO_3H_2^+$), combined with the use of invalid acidity functions. The reasonably good linear relation for the variation of rate with acidity extends over some five logarithmic units, however (Figure 1). Further work is required before a complete understanding is achieved of the effect of acidity on the equilibria and reaction rates of the chromium(VI)-alcohol acid reaction.

Conformational Effects on Alcohol Oxidation

The differing rates of oxidation of epimeric cyclohexanols by chromic acid can be of value in diagnosing conformation. The alcohol with the hydroxy group in the axial position (relatively unhindered C—H) is invariably oxidized faster than is its epimer,[34-36] usually by a

33. See also F. Holloway, *J. Am. Chem. Soc.*, **74**, 224 (1952).
34. G. Vavon and C. Zaremba, *Bull. soc. chim. France*, **49**, 1853 (1931).
35. J. Schreiber and A. Eschenmoser, *Helv. Chim. Acta*, **38**, 1529 (1955).
36. J. C. Richer, L. A. Pilato, and E. L. Eliel, *Chem. & Ind. (London)*, **1961**, 2007.

factor of 4 or 5. This is not simply a result of ready access by the oxidant to the equatorial C—H bond, however, since bulky groups in the vicinity of the bond cause further increases in oxidation rate. This can be illustrated, structures (III), by examining the rates of oxidation of the epimeric 2- and 4-t-butylcyclohexanols in which the bulky t-butyl group, by occupying an equatorial position, effectively controls the alcohol conformation.[36] Although the electronic effect of alkyl groups in accelerating the rate cannot be ignored, the steric effect of bulky groups is apparent in the examples shown.

(III)

These rate differences have been rationalized in terms of mechanism in different ways. Eschenmoser and Eliel have attributed the rate increases to a relief of steric strain in the transition state as the trigonal carbonyl group is being formed. Kwart, on the other hand, believes that a unimolecular decomposition of the chromate ester occurs and that the cyclic transition state is favored by the decrease in rotational freedom in the esters of hindered alcohols.[25, 37] He has pointed out that carbonyl stability does not seem to be an important factor in determining the rate of oxidation of an alcohol.

Tertiary Alcohols

The oxidation of tertiary alcohols can proceed only with carbon-carbon bond cleavage or with dehydration, and these are usually slower processes than the oxidation of carbon-hydrogen bonds in primary and secondary alcohols. Tertiary alcohols with an adjacent C—H group

37. H. Kwart, *Chem. & Ind. (London)*, **1962**, 610.

undergo rate-controlling dehydration in chromic acid solution, followed by rapid oxidation of the olefin to epoxide, which is then further degraded.[38]

$$(CH_3CH_2)_3COH \xrightarrow{H^+} (CH_3CH_2)_2C=CHCH_3 \xrightarrow{Cr^{VI}}$$

$$(CH_3CH_2)_2C \overset{O}{\underset{}{\diagup \diagdown}} CHCH_3 \xrightarrow{Cr^{VI}} \text{degradation products}$$

Alcohols that are unable to dehydrate undergo oxidative scissions expected of electron-deficient intermediates.[39]

$$(C_6H_5)_3COH \xrightarrow[HOAc]{Cr^{VI}} (C_6H_5)_2C=O$$

$$(C_6H_5)_3CCHOHC_6H_5 \xrightarrow[HOAc]{Cr^{VI}} (C_6H_5)_3COH + C_6H_5CHO$$

The cations

$$(C_6H_5)_3CO^+ \quad \text{and} \quad (C_6H_5)_3C\overset{O^+}{\overset{\|}{C}}HC_6H_5$$

which would rearrange or decompose to the observed products, are doubtless never fully formed. The transition state for cation generation almost certainly involves cleavage or rearrangement [paths A and B in Eq. (6)].

Light was shed on the mechanism of generation of the cations that cleave or rearrange by the study of the chromic acid oxidation of phenyl t-butyl carbinol [Eq. (5)].[40] The amount of cleavage product was greatly

$$C_6H_5CHOHt\text{-Bu} \xrightarrow[H^+]{Cr^{VI}} \begin{cases} C_6H_5C\overset{O}{\overset{\|}{}}t\text{-Bu} \\ C_6H_5CHO + t\text{-BuOH} \end{cases} \tag{5}$$

reduced by the addition of manganous or cerous ions, which are known to be excellent scavengers for chromium(IV) and chromium(V) intermediates. It seems likely, in view of other work,[11] that chromium(V) (or

38. W. F. Sager, *J. Am. Chem. Soc.*, **78**, 4970 (1956).
39. W. A. Mosher and E. Langerak, *J. Am. Chem. Soc.*, **73**, 1302 (1951); **71**, 286 (1949); L. S. Levitt, *J. Org. Chem.*, **20**, 1297 (1955).
40. J. Hampton, A. Leo, and F. H. Westheimer, *J. Am. Chem. Soc.*, **78**, 306 (1956).

IV) esters decompose to generate the rearranged or cleaved cations [Eq. (6)]. Chromium(VI) esters of tertiary alcohols probably also decompose in this way.

$$R_3CO-Cr^V-\begin{cases} \xrightarrow{A} R^+ + R_2C{=}O + Cr^{III} \searrow \\ \xrightarrow{B} R_2C{=}\overset{+}{O}R + Cr^{III} \nearrow \end{cases} R_2C{=}O + ROH + Cr^{III} \quad (6)$$

In certain cases it is clear that direct cleavage (path A), not rearrangement (path B), occurs. The oxidation of phenyl t-butyl carbinol in ^{18}O labeled water produces labeled t-butyl alcohol.[41] This cannot result from hemiacetal hydrolysis (path B), since the latter would yield unlabeled alcohol. Oxidation of alcohols such as triphenylcarbinol, however, probably proceeds via rearrangement rather than cleavage, since a phenyl cation is a very poor leaving group.

Even alcohols that can undergo dehydration or direct oxidation react by carbon-carbon bond cleavage if sufficiently stable carbonium ions can be generated [Eqs. (7) and (8)].

$$t\text{-BuCH}_2\overset{\overset{\displaystyle OH}{|}}{\underset{\overset{\displaystyle |}{CH_3}}{C}}CH_3 \xrightarrow[\text{HOAc}]{Cr^{VI}} CH_3\overset{\overset{\displaystyle OH}{|}}{\underset{\overset{\displaystyle |}{CH_3}}{C}}CH_2CH_3 + CH_3\overset{\overset{\displaystyle O}{||}}{C}CH_3 \quad (7)$$

$$t\text{-Bu}\overset{\overset{\displaystyle OH}{|}}{C}HCH_2CH_2CH_3 \xrightarrow[\text{HOAc}]{Cr^{VI}} t\text{-BuOH} + CH_3CH_2CH_2CHO \quad (8)$$

ALDEHYDES

The chromic acid oxidation of aldehydes is similar in many ways to the chromic acid–alcohol reaction.[5, 15, 42] The transition state is a monochromium species; there is a deuterium-isotope effect of 4.3 for the oxidation of C_6H_5CDO at $25°$; the effect of manganous and ceric ions is similar; and a similar effect of acids is observed, that is, $v = [RCHO][HCrO_4^-]h_0$.

41. J. J. Cawley and F. H. Westheimer, *Chem. & Ind (London)*, **1960**, 656. See also P. J. Lansbury, V. A. Pattison, and J. W. Diehl, *Chem. & Ind. (London)*, **1962**, 653.
42. H. C. S. Snethlage, *Rec. trav. chim.*, **60**, 877 (1941).

The chromate ester mechanism [Eq. (9)] accommodates these facts nicely. The ester in the equation here is that of the aldehyde hydrate, but it is a close analog of an alcohol, and its decomposition can be written as

$$RCHO + H^+ + HCrO_4^- \overset{K}{\rightleftharpoons} R-\underset{\underset{H}{|}}{\overset{\overset{OH}{|}}{C}}-OCrO_3H \overset{k}{\rightarrow} RCO_2H + Cr^{IV} \qquad (9)$$

a unimolecular or a bimolecular mechanism (see previous section). Formation of an aldehyde-chromate complex has been observed by Klaning.[43]

The two points of difference between the aldehyde and alcohol reactions are not unexpected. First, electron-withdrawing groups accelerate the aldehyde oxidation ($\rho = +1.02$),[5, 44] whereas they slow down the alcohol oxidation ($\rho = -1.0$ to -1.1). Second, replacing water with acetic acid as solvent does not cause the drastic increase in the rate that is observed in alcohol oxidation. Both these differences are probably due to the fact that an aldehyde must add a mole of water to attain the state in which it becomes formally equivalent to an alcohol. This step will have a fairly large positive rho, thus accounting for much of the difference in substituent effect in the two series. In addition, it eliminates the reversing mass-action effect of water on ester formation.

Roček has examined the oxidation of a series of aliphatic aldehydes that are either completely hydrated or have a known degree of hydration.[45] He finds a rho value (based on Taft's aliphatic sigma constants) of -1.2 for the chromium(VI) oxidation of the hydrates. This is close to the value obtained for the chromium(VI) oxidation of alcohols, and there is general agreement that the mechanisms are the same.

It is interesting that hemiacetals, which are similar in structure to aldehyde hydrates, are oxidized directly to esters and at rates that are greater than those of the aldehyde or alcohol alone. In fact, conversion of primary alcohols to esters can sometimes be conveniently accomplished by chromic acid oxidation, via the hemiacetal, one presumes [Eqs. (10)].[46] The relative ease of oxidation of functional groups is considered in the Appendix.

43. U. Klaning, *Acta Chem. Scand.*, **11**, 1313 (1957).
44. E. Luchi, *Gazz. chim. ital.*, **71**, 729, 752 (1941).
45. J. Roček, *Tet. Let.*, **5**, 1 (1959).
46. W. A. Mosher and D. M. Preiss, *J. Am. Chem. Soc.*, **75**, 5605 (1953); J. C. Craig, E. G. Davis, and J. S. Lake, *J. Chem. Soc.*, **1954**, 1874.

$$RCH_2OH \xrightarrow{Cr^{VI}} RCHO$$

$$RCHO + RCH_2OH \underset{}{\overset{H^+}{\rightleftharpoons}} R - \overset{\displaystyle OH}{\underset{\displaystyle H}{\overset{|}{\underset{|}{C}}}} - OR \xrightarrow{Cr^{VI}} R - \overset{\displaystyle O}{\overset{\|}{C}} - OR \qquad (10)$$

The competition experiments of Wiberg and Richardson[11] have been referred to earlier. They determined the reactivities of the intermediate chromium species with aromatic aldehydes and wrote Eqs. (11)

$$RCHO + Cr^{IV} \rightarrow R\underset{\bullet}{C}{=}O + Cr^{III}$$

$$R\underset{\bullet}{C}{=}O + Cr^{VI} \rightarrow RCO_2H + Cr^{V}$$

$$RCHO + Cr^{V} \rightarrow R - \overset{\displaystyle OH}{\underset{\displaystyle H}{\overset{|}{\underset{|}{C}}}} - OCr^{V} \qquad (11)$$

$$R - \overset{\displaystyle OH}{\underset{\displaystyle H}{\overset{|}{\underset{|}{C}}}} - OCr^{V} \rightarrow RCO_2H + Cr^{III}$$

to describe these exceedingly fast reactions. The decomposition of the chromium(V) ester in the final step, like similar reactions written earlier, can be written as a unimolecular or as a bimolecular mechanism; the latter requires a base to remove the proton.

HYDROCARBONS

Hydrocarbons and ethers, unlike alcohols and aldehydes, are unable to form esters with chromic acid, and their oxidation rates are, in general, much less.[47, 48] The polymeric state of chromium seems to have little effect on the oxidation rates of hydrocarbons and ethers; i.e., altering the chromium(VI) concentration, which in turn alters the proportion of monochromate and dichromate in the system, causes virtually no change

47. W. F. Sager and A. Bradley, *J. Am. Chem. Soc.*, **78**, 1187 (1956).
48. F. Mares and J. Roček, *Collection Czechoslov. Chem. Commun.*, **26**, 2370 (1961).

Table 4-1   *Relative rates of chromium(VI) oxidation, hydrogen abstraction, and chloride solvolysis*

Compound	Cr^{VI} oxidation	H· abstraction by CCl_3	Solvolysis of corresponding chloride
$C_6H_5CH_3$	1.0	1.0	1.0
$C_6H_5CH_2CH_3$	3.1	3.0	100
$(C_6H_5)_2CH_2$	6.3	8.0	2,000
$(C_6H_5)_3CH$	8.1	16.7	10,000,000

in the rate constant. Wiberg and Evans[12] believe that this distinguishes the chromium(VI) oxidations that proceed via an ester mechanism [rate a function of monomeric chromium(VI) concentration] from those that do not [rate a function of total chromium(VI) concentration].

Tertiary C—H groups in the hydrocarbons produce tertiary alcohols, whereas, if only methylene groups are present, ketones are formed.[47] The chromium(VI) oxidation of diphenylmethane to benzophenone has the following characteristics:[12] There is an isotope effect of 6.6 for the oxidation of $(C_6H_5)_2CD_2$, the rho value is negative ($\rho = -1.4$), and the reaction follows the rate law

$$v = k[(C_6H_5)_2CH_2]\,[Cr^{VI}]h_0$$

Wiberg and Evans have pointed out that the relative rates of oxidation of hydrocarbons tend to parallel their rates of reaction with hydrogen-atom abstractors. The heterolytic reactions of the corresponding halides, on the other hand, are widely different. Table 4-1 illustrates this.

Mares and Roček have compared the oxidation rates of the bicyclic hydrocarbons, camphane and isocamphane, with the solvolysis rates of the corresponding chlorides.[48] Neighbouring group participation, which would be expected if carbonium ions are formed, is clearly absent in the oxidation reactions. The oxidation rates of aliphatic hydrocarbons, on the other hand, are similar to the chloride solvolysis rates,[49] but this may simply reflect the change from tetra- to tricoordinated carbon in both reactions. The fact that cycloalkanes in acetic acid give the alcohols or

49. F. Mares, J. Roček, and J. Sicher, *Collection Czechoslov. Chem. Commun.*, **26**, 2355 (1961).

ketones, not the fairly stable acetates, is further indication that radicals, not carbonium ions, are intermediates.

Roček[50] has pointed out several pieces of evidence that are more compatible with carbonium ion than with radical intermediates—the absence of the dimer $Ar_2CHCHAr_2$ in the oxidation of Ar_2CH_2,[12] the trapping of carbonium ions in certain cases,[49, 51] the rearrangements that in a few cases accompany the oxidation.[48]

The above evidence suggests that neither carbonium ions nor radicals are discrete intermediates, and the demonstration by Wiberg and Foster of a high degree of retention of configuration in the chromium(VI) oxidation of (+)-3-methylheptane to (+)-3-methyl-3-heptanol confirms this.[52] They suggest that a hydrogen-atom transfer occurs, giving two radicals in a solvent cage, which may then either diffuse apart or combine to give a chromium(IV) ester [Eq. (12)]. The latter, which was

$$R_3CH + Cr^{VI} \rightarrow \underset{\substack{\text{solvent} \\ \text{cage}}}{[R_3C \cdot Cr^V]} \xrightarrow{\substack{\text{diffuse} \\ \text{apart}}} R_3C \cdot \xrightarrow{Cr^{VI}} R_3C^+$$

$$R_3C\!-\!O\!-\!Cr^{IV} \rightarrow R_3COH \qquad\qquad \underset{\text{olefin}}{\overset{\displaystyle R_3COH}{+}} \qquad (12)$$

also considered as a reaction intermediate by Slack and Waters,[53] can cleave either at the Cr—O bond to give the alcohol with retention of configuration or at the C—O bond to give partial racemization. It is significant that hydrolysis of a chromium(IV) ester has been shown to occur with chromium-oxygen bond cleavage.[52] The radical pair here need have only a very short lifetime. The lifetime cannot be vanishingly small, however, because this would correspond to an insertion of an oxygen in the carbon-hydrogen bond, producing pentacoordinated carbon in the transition state. The lack of steric retardation eliminates this possibility.

The bond breaking and bond making that accompany the conversion of hydrocarbon and chromic acidium ion to Cr^{IV} ester in this scheme may be depicted as in Eq. (13).

It is not obvious why the chromic acidium ion should be so much better as a hydrogen-atom abstractor than neutral chromic acid. However, an analogous situation exists in the permanganate-alcohol reaction

50. J. Roček, *Tet. Let.*, **4**, 135 (1962).
51. I. Necsoiu and C. D. Nenitzescu, *Chem. & Ind.* (*London*), **1960**, 377.
52. K. B. Wiberg and G. Foster, *J. Am. Chem. Soc.*, **83**, 423 (1961); *Chem. & Ind.*, **1961**, 108.
53. R. Slack and W. A. Waters, *J. Chem. Soc.*, **1949**, 599.

where there is some indication that the alkoxide ion may be a much better hydrogen-atom donor than the neutral alcohol (Chapter 5).

$$(13)$$

OLEFINS AND GLYCOLS

Chromic acid oxidation of olefins, which is first-order in each reagent,[54] produces epoxides, glycols, and eventually cleavage products.[55-57] Rearrangements may accompany the oxidation, resulting in the formation of carboxylic acids having the same number of carbons as the original alkene.[58]

$$(t\text{-BuCH}_2)_2C{=}CH_2 \xrightarrow{\text{Cr}^{\text{VI}}} (t\text{-BuCH}_2)_2CHCO_2H$$

Similarly, tetramethylethylene gives t-butyl methyl ketone.[55]

$$(CH_3)_2C{=}C(CH_3)_2 \xrightarrow{\text{Cr}^{\text{VI}}} (CH_3)_3C\overset{\displaystyle O}{\overset{\|}{C}}CCH_3$$

The rearrangements, surprisingly, do not proceed via the glycols.

The cleavage of cis glycols [Eq. (14)] is much faster than that of their trans isomers, suggesting a cyclic ester intermediate[59, 60] analogous to that which is believed to form with glycol-cleaving reagents, such as periodic acid (Chapter 8). Some important differences exist between the

54. H. H. Zeiss and F. R. Zwanzig, *J. Am. Chem. Soc.*, **79**, 1733 (1957).
55. W. J. Hickinbottom, D. R. Hogg, D. Peters, and D. G. M. Wood, *J. Chem. Soc.*, **1954**, 4400.
56. J. H. Gorvin, *J. Chem. Soc.*, **1959**, 678.
57. R. Slack and W. A. Waters, *J. Chem. Soc.*, **1949**, 594.
58. A. Butlerow, *J. Russ. Phys. Chem. Soc.*, **12**, 1482 (1879).
59. J. Roček and F. H. Westheimer, *J. Am. Chem. Soc.*, **84**, 2241 (1962).
60. A. C. Chatterji and S. K. Mukherjee, *Z. physik. Chem.*, **207**, 372 (1957).

chromic acid and periodic acid reactions, however. For example, increasing the number of alkyl groups on the glycol causes first an increase and then a decrease in the rate of the periodic acid cleavage, whereas it causes a continuous increase in the rate of the chromic acid cleavage.

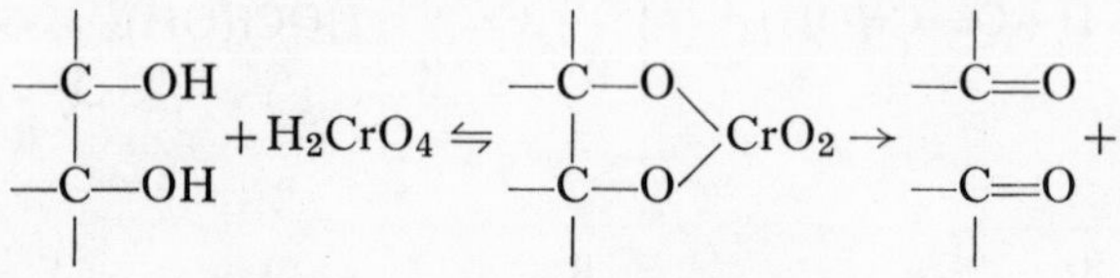

$$
\begin{array}{l}
\overset{|}{-\text{C}}-\text{OH} \\
\overset{|}{-\text{C}}-\text{OH} \\
\overset{|}{}
\end{array}
+ \text{H}_2\text{CrO}_4 \leftrightharpoons
\begin{array}{l}
\overset{|}{-\text{C}}-\text{O} \\
\overset{|}{-\text{C}}-\text{O}
\end{array}
\!\!\!\!\!>\!\!\text{CrO}_2 \rightarrow
\begin{array}{l}
\overset{|}{-\text{C}}=\text{O} \\
\overset{|}{-\text{C}}=\text{O} \\
\overset{|}{}
\end{array}
+ \text{Cr}^{\text{IV}} \qquad (14)
$$

This is believed to be due to the fact that the chromium diester is in rapid equilibrium with starting materials, and its cleavage is accelerated by electron-donating alkyl groups, which would help stabilize the incipient

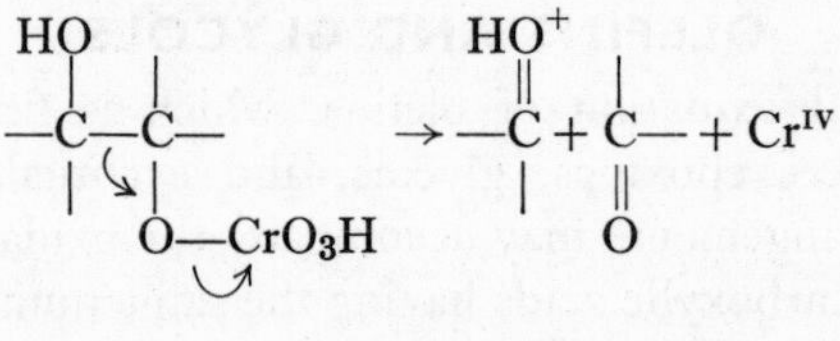

$$
\begin{array}{c}
\text{HO} \\
\overset{|}{-\text{C}}-\overset{|}{\text{C}}- \\
\overset{|}{\underset{\curvearrowleft}{}} | \\
\text{O}-\text{CrO}_3\text{H}
\end{array}
\rightarrow
\begin{array}{c}
\text{HO}^+ \\
\parallel \\
-\text{C}+\overset{|}{\text{C}}- \\
\overset{|}{}\ \ \parallel \\
\ \ \ \ \text{O}
\end{array}
+ \text{Cr}^{\text{IV}} \qquad (15)
$$

carbonyls in the transition state. With periodic acid, the formation of the ester becomes rate-controlling when glycol is completely substituted with alkyl groups.

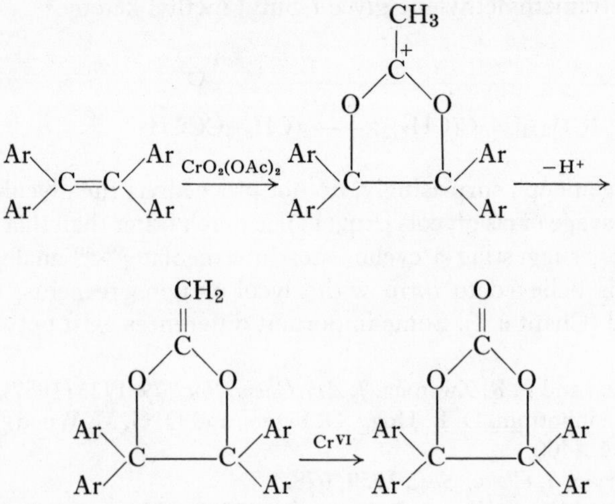

$$(16)$$

The cleavage of *trans* glycols [Eq. (15)] probably involves a concerted mechanism similar to that suggested for the lead tetraacetate–*trans* glycol reaction (page 100).

A second difference between chromic acid and the conventional glycol-cleaving reagents is the former's ability to oxidize a glycol-containing primary or secondary hydroxyl to a hydroxy aldehyde or ketone rather than to carbon-carbon cleavage products.[59-61]

The diacid chloride of chromic acid—chromyl chloride, CrO_2Cl_2, whose reactions are considered in more detail in the next section—is also able to cleave glycols.[57] The diacetate of chromic acid—chromyl acetate, $CrO_2(OAc)_2$—converts tetraarylethylenes to carbonates, probably via the path in Eq. (16).[62] Hickinbottom's work, however, shows that Cr^{VI}-Ac_2O systems (equivalent to chromyl acetate) give chiefly epoxides with other olefins.[55, 63]

ÉTARD REACTION

The conversion of toluene to benzaldehyde by chromyl chloride was discovered some eighty years ago by Étard.[64] The reaction involves formation of a dark amorphous complex between the hydrocarbon and 2 moles of the oxidant, and this, on hydrolysis, gives the aldehyde.

$$C_6H_5CH_3 + 2CrO_2Cl_2 \rightarrow C_6H_5CH_3 \cdot 2CrO_2Cl_2 \xrightarrow{H_2O} C_6H_5CHO$$

The reaction can also be performed conveniently by using CrO_3 in an acetic anhydride–acetic acid solution, the oxidant in this case presumably being chromyl acetate.[65, 66]

Aliphatic hydrocarbons, particularly those with tertiary carbons, also react, but in these cases rearrangements and deep-seated oxidations may also occur.[67]

Apart from the obvious question about the identity of the complex, there are other features of this interesting reaction that require explanation in terms of mechanism. For example, the oxidation of n-propyl benzene gives 1-phenyl-1-chloropropane, propiophenone, and benzyl methyl ketone as major products.[68, 69] The last compound involves

61. A. C. Chatterji and S. K. Mukherjee, *Z. physik. Chem.*, **210**, 166 (1959).
62. W. A. Mosher, F. W. Steffgen, and P. J. Lansbury, *J. Org. Chem.*, **26**, 670 (1961).
63. M. A. Davis and W. J. Hickinbottom, *J. Chem. Soc.*, **1958**, 2205, and earlier papers.
64. A. Étard, *Ann. chim. et phys.*, **22**, 218 (1881).
65. K. L. Kraus, *Angew. Chem.*, **70**, 502 (1958).
66. J. Roček and F. Sorm, *Chem. listy*, **49**, 306 (1955).
57. C. C. Hobbs, Jr., and B. Houston, *J. Am. Chem. Soc.*, **76**, 1254 (1954).
68. K. B. Wiberg, B. Marshall, and G. Foster, *Tet. Let.*, **8**, 345 (1962).
69. W. v. Miller and G. Rohde, *Ber.*, **23**, 1070 (1890).

oxidation at a secondary carbon that is one removed from the active benzylic position, despite the fact that benzylic positions (or tertiary carbons) are normally the ones that are readily attacked. For instance, t-butylbenzene has no benzylic hydrogens, and it reacts slowly, indeed.[70]

$$C_6H_5CH_2CH_2CH_3 \xrightarrow[\text{2. } H_2O]{\text{1. } CrO_2Cl_2}$$

$$\underset{C_6H_5\overset{\displaystyle O}{\overset{\|}{C}}CH_2CH_3}{} + \underset{C_6H_5CH_2\overset{\displaystyle O}{\overset{\|}{C}}CH_3}{} + C_6H_5CHClCH_2CH_3$$

The proportion of products in this reaction depends on the concentration of chromyl chloride. When the latter is low, the propiophenone–benzyl methyl ketone ratio is low; when the chromyl chloride concentration is raised, the product ratio rises too.[68]

Wiberg, Marshall, and Foster[68] have written the mechanism in Eq. (17) that accommodates these facts. The initial step is believed to be hydrogen-atom abstraction[71] from the benzylic carbon by a chromyl chloride molecule, giving a transient intermediate (I) which can either collapse to form a chromium (IV) ester (II) or abstract a chlorine atom to form the chloride (III). [The formation of the chromium(IV) ester from hydrocarbon is, thus, analogous to the mechanism proposed for the hydrocarbon–chromic acid reaction, page 52.] The

$$C_6H_5CH_2CH_2CH_3 + CrO_2Cl_2 \rightarrow [C_6H_5\overset{\cdot}{C}HCH_2CH_3 + Cr(OH)OCl_2]$$
(I)

$$\begin{array}{cc}
C_6H_5CHCH_2CH_3 & C_6H_5CHClCH_2CH_3 + Cr(OH)OCl \\
| & \\
OCr(OH)Cl_2 & (III) \qquad\qquad (17) \\
(II) &
\end{array}$$

intermediate (II) then either undergoes an elimination reaction [Eq. (18)] to give β-methylstyrene (IV) or, if the concentration of free chromyl chloride is high, undergoes further substitution to give the complex (V).

70. O. H. Wheeler, *Can. J. Chem.*, **38**, 2137 (1960).
71. The effect of varying the solvent on the rate of the toluene–chromyl chloride reaction suggests that the transition state for the reaction has little ionic character in agreement with the hydrogen-atom abstraction mechanism written here. [R. A. Stairs, *Can. J. Chem.*, **40**, 1656 (1962).]

The latter is the "normal complex" (corresponding to that obtained in the case of toluene), and its hydrolysis gives the expected product, propiophenone (VII). β-Methylstyrene has been shown to react with chromyl chloride to give benzyl methyl ketone (VI)[68] and it is reasonable

$$\begin{array}{c}
\overset{\displaystyle O}{\underset{\displaystyle \| }{}} \\
C_6H_5CH{=}CHCH_3 \xrightarrow[\text{2. }H_2O]{\text{1. }CrO_2Cl_2} C_6H_5CH_2CCH_3 \\
\text{(IV)} \qquad\qquad\qquad \text{(VI)}
\end{array}$$

(II)   (18)

$$\begin{array}{c}
\underset{\displaystyle OCr(OH)Cl_2}{\overset{\displaystyle OCr(OH)Cl_2}{C_6H_5CCH_2CH_3}} \xrightarrow{H_2O} C_6H_5\overset{\displaystyle O}{\overset{\displaystyle \|}{C}}CH_2CH_3 \\
\text{(V)} \qquad\qquad\qquad \text{(VII)}
\end{array}$$

with CrO$_2$Cl$_2$ on (II)

to assume that this is the source of the product in this case. It is interesting

that the oxidation of $C_6H_5CH_2CD_2CH_3$ produces $C_6H_5CHD\overset{\displaystyle O}{\overset{\displaystyle \|}{C}}CH_3$ in fair yield, showing that a hydrogen migration has occurred,[68] probably in the conversion of (IV) to (VI).

chapter five | Permanganate Oxidations

Potassium permanganate is probably the most powerful of the oxidizing agents in the organic chemist's armory. Its reversible electrode potential for the 5-electron reduction to manganese(II) is 1.5 volts. Reversible electrode potentials usually give only a rough idea of an oxidizing agent's strength in practical terms, because the vast majority of organic oxidations proceed under nonequilibrium conditions. Hence, the rates of these reactions may vary widely, depending on the structure of the substrate and the presence of catalytic species, particularly acids and bases.

The great reactivity of permanganate as an oxidant is reflected in its ability to use different reaction paths, depending on the structure of the organic substrate, and depending on the acidity and basicity of the solution.[1,2] Low enthalpies of activation, frequently in the range 5 to 10 kcal mole^{-1}, are further indications of the desire of permanganate to lower its chemical potential. Even those reactions that are extremely slow, the permanganate oxidation of alcohols in neutral solution, for example, are slow because of extremely negative activation entropies, not because of unfavorable heats of activation.

Permanganate oxidations invariably exhibit negative entropies of activation, usually in the range -15 to -40 e.u. The large variation in rates of oxidation of certain compounds that accompanies pH changes is caused in the main by variations in the entropy term. This in turn, is

1. W. A. Waters, *Quart. Revs. (London)*, **1958**, 277.
2. J. W. Ladbury and C. F. Cullis, *Chem. Revs.*, **58**, 403 (1958).

caused chiefly by the concentration of the substrate (the alkoxide ion for alcohol oxidation) being drastically altered by changes in pH.

Permanganate may lower its chemical potential in any of several ways. First, it may react by electron abstraction; this reaction path accounts for the very rapid permanganate-manganate exchange reaction in solution.

$$*MnO_4^- + MnO_4^= \rightleftharpoons *MnO_4^= + MnO_4^-$$

Second, it may abstract a hydrogen atom from a likely donor and form the acid manganate ion $HMnO_4^-$.

$$MnO_4^- + RH \rightarrow HMnO_4^- + R\cdot$$

Reactions of this type have been suggested in some cases, and these are discussed later. Third, a hydride ion may be removed from the substrate. Anions of organic compounds might be expected to prefer this path.

$$MnO_4^- + ZH^- \rightarrow HMnO_4^= + Z$$

Finally, oxygen donation by permanganate to an organic substrate is possible.

$$MnO_4^- + Z \rightarrow MnO_3^- + ZO$$

The net changes in the permanganate-olefin reaction can be represented in this way, although, as will be seen later, the oxygen donation occurs via a cyclic transition state in which two permanganate oxygens are bound to the olefin.

Virtually all kinetic investigations of permanganate oxidations have been carried out in aqueous solution, although studies in aqueous acetic acid have occasionally been made. This is because permanganate attacks to some degree all organic solvents in which it is soluble. The characteristic purple color of permanganate is due to the tetrahedral paramagnetic ion, MnO_4^-, of the strong acid $HMnO_4$. It exchanges its oxygens with the aqueous solvent rapidly in acid solution but more slowly in neutral and alkaline solution. This permits the use of oxygen-18 as tracer in all but acidic solutions.

Reduction Products

The green manganate ion $MnO_4^=$ is unstable in solutions more acidic than about pH 12, and, even in quite alkaline solution, very slow disproportionation to permanganate and manganese dioxide is observed. The equivalent weight of potassium permanganate in an oxidation process thus depends on the pH of the solution. In strongly basic solution, manganate accumulates, and the net equivalent change is one unit. In neutral solution, the manganate disproportionates, and MnO_2 is produced, corresponding to a 3-equivalent reaction. Manganate often seems to be formed directly from permanganate by a 1-equivalent reaction and, indeed, it often can be precipitated almost instantaneously, as the highly insoluble barium salt. An initial 2-equivalent step producing manganese(V) may nevertheless be occurring, since it is known that the Mn^{VII}-Mn^V reaction is exceedingly fast.[3, 4]

Manganate ion exchanges its oxygen atoms with the solvent in aqueous alkaline solution much less rapidly than does permanganate.[5]

With one exception, the oxidation of organic substrates by manganate is much slower than those by permanganate, e.g., the relative oxidation rates by MnO_4^- and $MnO_4^=$ of benzhydrol, $(C_6H_5)_2CHOH$, are 40 : 1.[6] The one exception is the oxidation of aromatic aldehydes, for which a series of substituted benzaldehydes gave almost identical rates with manganate and permanganate, the fate of the manganese being MnO_2 in each case.[7]

Potassium manganate has been used as a dihydroxylating agent for double bonds,[8] and it is said to be superior to permanganate in this respect, although it is probably inferior to osmium tetroxide.

The blue hypomanganate ion MnO_4^{3-} is stable only in very strongly alkaline solution.[9, 4] In solutions less alkaline than 10-molar potassium hydroxide, it disproportionates to manganate and manganese dioxide. It is suspected of playing a role as an intermediate in permanganate oxidations, since a 2-equivalent reduction of the latter will produce Mn^V. Its extreme instability under normal reaction conditions makes it virtually impossible to detect in most permanganate oxidations, however.

Manganese dioxide is the usual product of reduction of permanganate in all but strongly basic solution; in the latter solutions, manganate fails to disproportionate. Although its solubility is low, the precipitation of MnO_2 may be long delayed in the presence of phosphate ions. The manganese dioxide produced by reduction of permanganate in aqueous solution is a rather feeble oxidant, but, in acid solutions, certain

3. A. Carrington and M. C. R. Symons, *J. Chem. Soc.*, **1956**, 3373.
4. J. S. F. Pode and W. A. Waters, *J. Chem. Soc.*, **1956**, 717.
5. H. O. McDonald, *Diss. Abs.*, **21**, 454 (1960); compare M. C. R. Symons, *J. Chem. Soc.*, **1954**, 3676.
6. R. Stewart, *J. Am. Chem. Soc.*, **79**, 3057 (1957).
7. K. B. Wiberg and R. Stewart, *J. Am. Chem. Soc.*, **77**, 1786 (1955).
8. W. Rigby, *J. Chem. Soc.*, **1956**, 2452.
9. H. Lux, *Z. Naturforsch.*, **1**, 281 (1946).

reductants such as iodide and oxalate reduce it to manganese(II). Manganese dioxide is a convenient reagent for the oxidation of α,β-unsaturated alcohols to aldehydes and ketones, but the heterogeneous nature of the reaction makes elucidation of the mechanism difficult.[10]

HYDROCARBON OXIDATIONS

The autoxidation of tetralin can be initiated by potassium permanganate (as well as by chromic acid and periodic acid).[11] Presumably, the oxidant abstracts a hydrogen atom from the activated benzylic carbon of tetralin to initiate the chain.

When potassium permanganate and naphthalene are refluxed in a large excess of acetic anhydride, α-naphthylacetic acid is produced in good yield.[11]

In a similar way, β-naphthol gives 2-hydroxy-1-naphthylacetic acid, n-propyl benzene gives 3,4-diphenylhexane, and acetic anhydride, alone, gives succinic anhydride [Eq. (1)].[12]

$$
\begin{array}{c}
CH_3-C\diagdown{}^O_O \\
| \\
CH_3-C\diagdown{}^O_O
\end{array}
\xrightarrow{KMnO_4}
\begin{array}{c}
CH_2-C\diagdown{}^O_O \\
| \\
CH_2-C\diagdown{}^O_O
\end{array}
\tag{1}
$$

There can be little doubt that abstraction of hydrogen atoms by the oxidant produces radicals that couple to give these products. Whether or not the active oxidant is permanganate or a manganese species of intermediate valence is not known, however, The latter are the active oxidants

10. R. M. Evans, *Quart. Revs. (London)*, **1959**, 61.
11. W. A. Waters, *Trans. Faraday Soc.*, **42**, 184 (1946).
12. W. Griehl, *Ber.*, **80**, 410 (1947).

in several reactions to be discussed later in the chapter, and a diagnostic test for their participation in the oxidation is the effect of added manganous ion on the reaction rate. Manganous ion and permanganate react rapidly to produce ions of intermediate oxidation state, Mn^{III} and Mn^{IV} (Guyard reaction).[2] Reactions that are rapidly accelerated by added amounts of manganous salts are assumed to involve these ions, particularly Mn^{III}. The latter can be complexed tightly by fluoride, and many permanganate oxidations that actually proceed by a Mn^{III} reaction can be severely inhibited by addition of fluoride ions.

The oxidation of alkylbenzenes by permanganate produces benzoic acid, but some degradation of the ring often occurs.[13] The effect of added ions indicates that here, too, manganese(III) ions are the active oxidants. Electron-donating groups in the ring facilitate the oxidation of toluene to benzoic acids in aqueous acetic acid, but a Hammett plot for meta and para methyl, chloro, and nitro toluenes shows only a rough fit ($\rho \approx -1.5$). Furthermore, the activation entropies vary rather widely.

OLEFIN DIHYDROXYLATION

Although the reaction of potassium permanganate with olefins to produce diols has been largely superseded by the use of osmium tetroxide in recent years, the reaction retains some importance. The reaction is also of historical interest in that the cis mode of addition of the hydroxyl groups was at first thought to confirm the intuitively attractive idea of cis addition of reagents to double bonds. Cis addition has since been shown

$$\begin{array}{c}\diagup C \diagdown \\ \| \quad +MnO_4^- \longrightarrow \\ \diagup C \diagdown\end{array} \qquad \begin{array}{c} -C-O \\ \quad\quad\quad MnO_2^- \\ -C-O \end{array} \xrightarrow{H_2O} \begin{array}{c} -C-OH \\ \quad\quad\quad +Mn^V \\ -C-OH \end{array} \qquad (2)$$

to be exceptional and is confined largely to those reagents, like permanganate and osmium tetroxide, that can form cyclic esters. Wagner[14] first suggested that a cyclic ester might be formed in the reaction, and the stereochemical work of Boeseken[15] lent strong support to this idea [Eq. (2)]. Reasonable yields of diol are obtained only in alkaline medium, and this is, at first consideration, surprising, since the oxidation of alcohols by permanganate is strongly base-catalyzed. There are two reasons for this situation, however. First, the reaction between olefins and permanganate

13. C. F. Cullis and J. W. Ladbury, *J. Chem. Soc.*, **1955**, 555, 1407, 2850, 4186.
14. G. Wagner, *J. Russ. Phys. Chem. Soc.*, **27**, 219 (1895).
15. J. Boeseken, *Rec. trav. chim.*, **40**, 553 (1921).

is faster than the oxidation of most alcohols even in basic solution. Second, if the hydroxyl concentration becomes too low, the reaction tends to produce α-hydroxy ketones rather than the diol.[16] It is known that these are not produced by further degradation of the diol, and it is reasonable to assume, as have Wiberg and Saegebarth,[17] that a common intermediate exists for the production of diol and hydroxy ketone. Their work with [18]O has provided further confirmation of the cyclic ester-reaction path, since the oxygen in the diol has been shown to arise chiefly from the permanganate. The concentration of [18]O found in the diol is actually somewhat less than two equivalents per mole, but this is not unexpected in view of the oxygen exchange between water manganate and permanganate which occurs in alkaline solution.[5]

The reaction path shown in Eq. (3) has been worked out by Wiberg and Saegebarth for the olefin-permanganate reaction. The competition

between hydroxyl ion and permanganate for the intermediate hydroxy-manganese(V) ester accounts for the dependence of product distribution on the basicity of the medium.

ALCOHOLS

The oxidation of primary and secondary alcohols by permanganate proceeds very slowly in neutral solution but is usually very rapid in alkaline and strongly acid solution. The oxidation of benzhydrol, $(C_6H_5)_2CHOH$, has been thoroughly investigated in neutral and basic solution, and the results may be summarized as follows:[18]

1. The reaction obeys the following kinetic law:

$$\text{Rate} = k[\text{alcohol}] [\text{MnO}_4^-] [\text{OH}^-]$$

16. R. U. Lemieux and E. von Rudloff, *Can. J. Chem.*, **33**, 1701 (1955).
17. K. B. Wiberg and K. A. Saegebarth, *J. Am. Chem. Soc.*, **79**, 2822 (1957).
18. R. Stewart, *J. Am. Chem. Soc.*, **79**, 3057 (1957).

2. An isotope effect of 6.6:1 at 25° is observed when benzhydrol-d, $(C_6H_5)_2CDOH$, is oxidized.

3. A positive kinetic salt effect is observed.

4. The product benzophenone contains no oxygen derived from the oxidant.

These results suggest the following mechanism in which a hydride ion is transferred from the alkoxide ion to permanganate to produce the ketone together with a manganese(V) species, and this mechanism was originally thought to be correct.[18] The driving force in a hydride expulsion mechanism would be the negative charge on oxygen.

$$(C_6H_5)_2CHOH + OH^- \rightleftharpoons (C_6H_5)_2CHO^- + H_2O \qquad \text{rapid equilibrium}$$

$$(C_6H_5)_2CHO^- + MnO_4^- \rightarrow (C_6H_5)_2C{=}O + HMnO_4^= \qquad \text{slow}$$

$$HMnO_4^= + MnO_4^- + OH^- \rightarrow 2MnO_4^= + H_2O \qquad \text{fast}$$

Benzhydrol, like most alcohols, is so feebly acidic that the pre-equilibrium step in this mechanism is not very far to the right even in fairly alkaline solution. The increased acidity of fluorinated alcohols allows what has been assumed to be the rate-controlling step, to be examined separately.

The alcohols $ArCHOHCF_3$, $(CF_3)_2CHOH$, and CF_3CH_2OH are acidic enough to be virtually completely ionized in 0.2 M KOH, and, in agreement with the above mechanism, the oxidation rate of these alcohols has essentially reached its maximum value in this solution.[19]

There are two very curious aspects to the oxidation of the fluoro alcohols, however. First, the isotope effects observed with the deuterio compounds $(C_6H_5)_2CDOHCF_3$[20] and $(CF_3)_2CDOH$[21] are extraordinarily large, being 16:1 for the former (and its m-Br and p-CH$_3$ derivatives) and 19:1 for the latter at 25°. Either proton tunneling is occurring, or the bending modes of the C—H bond have been drastically changed in the transition state in addition to the stretching mode.[22-24] The presence of strongly electron-withdrawing groups is undoubtedly a factor in increasing the size of the isotope effect, as can be seen by an

19. R. Stewart and R. Van der Linden, *Discussions Faraday Soc.*, **1960**, 211.
20. R. Stewart and R. Van der Linden, *Tet. Let.*, **2**, 28 (1960).
21. R. Stewart and M. Mocek, unpublished results.
22. L. Melander, *Isotope Effects on Reaction Rates*, Ronald, New York, 1960, p. 22.
23. R. P. Bell, J. A. Fendley, and J. R. Hulett, *Proc. Roy. Soc. (London)*, **235A**, 453 (1956); J. R. Hulett, *Proc. Roy. Soc. (London)*, **251A**, 274 (1959).
24. E. F. Caldin and E. Harbron, *J. Chem. Soc.*, **1962**, 3454.

examination of the chromic acid–alcohol reaction (Chapter 4). The precise connection between electron-withdrawing character and either change of the bending modes or proton tunneling is difficult to see, however, particularly when one realizes that the active species, the anions, also contain a strongly electron-donating group, the negatively charged oxygen anion, [structure (I)].

$$CF_3 \leftarrow \overset{\overset{\displaystyle O^-}{|}}{\underset{\underset{\displaystyle CF_3}{\downarrow}}{C}}\text{---H---}MnO_4^-$$

(I)

Whatever the precise cause of the anomolous isotope effects, it is clear that the C—H bond is being broken in the rate-controlling step.

The second unusual aspect of the permanganate oxidation of fluoro alcohols is the extremely small, almost negligible, effect of substituents in the aromatic ring on the rate of oxidation of compounds of structure

$$Z \underset{}{\overset{}{\bigcirc}}\text{---CHOHCF}_3$$

when the rate-controlling step, only, is considered.[19] The oxidation rates of a series of meta- and para-substituted alcohols differ considerably at pH 10, the meta-nitro compound reacting fastest and the para-methoxy compound slowest ($\rho = 1.0$). This difference in rate turns out to be caused almost entirely by the effect of substituents on the ionization of the alcohol. The rates at pH 13, where all the alcohols are virtually completely ionized, are very little different ($\rho \approx 0$).

A hydride expulsion should be favored by electron-donating groups and should result in a large negative Hammett rho value.[25] (The rho values for hydride *addition* to the carbonyl group of substituted aceto-phenones and fluorenones are $+2.6$[26] and $+2.65$,[27] respectively; these values are large and positive, as expected.) The intuitively attractive hydride transfer mechanism is thus at variance with the size of the Hammett rho value and with the Swain criterion (page 24). Other mechanisms that are accommodated by the kinetics must, therefore, be considered.

25. L. P. Hammett, *Physical Organic Chemistry*, McGraw-Hill, New York, 1940, p. 185.
26. H. C. Brown, A. Tsukamoto, and T. Kawanami, personal communication.
27. G. G. Smith and R. P. Boyer, *Tetrahedron*, **18**, 323 (1962).

The rate law for the permanganate oxidation of alcohols in basic solution can be accommodated by various termolecular mechanisms involving solvent molecules as proton abstractors.[20] However, there is no solvent isotope effect when D_2O is used.[19, 21] The change in the hydrogen-oxygen vibrational frequency that would occur as the H_2O changes to H_3O^+ would be expected to result in a discernible solvent isotope effect and these possible reaction paths will not be further discussed here.

It seems certain that the rate-controlling step in the permanganate oxidation of alcohols is between the alkoxide ion and permanganate ion. Finally, then, the mechanism in Eq. (4), hydrogen-atom abstraction by permanaganate from the alkoxide ion, should be considered. This

$$\underset{\overset{|}{H}}{\overset{\overset{O^-}{|}}{Ar-C}}-CF_3 + MnO_4^- \rightarrow \overset{\overset{O^-}{|}}{\underset{\overset{|}{\underset{Mn^{VII}\,or\,Mn^{VI}}{\xrightarrow{\text{fast}}}}}{Ar-\overset{\bullet}{C}}}-CF_3 + HMnO_4^-$$

$$\xrightarrow{\text{fast}} \underset{}{Ar-\overset{\overset{O}{\|}}{C}-CF_3} \qquad (4)$$

mechanism accommodates all the facts known about the reaction, in particular the small effect of ring substituents. However, it is not immediately obvious why there should be such enormous differences in the oxidation rates of the neutral alcohols and their anions.

Two points are worth consideration in this respect. First, an examination of the chemistry of the radicals produced by a hydrogen abstraction process reveals, in fact, that precisely such an effect should be observed. Porter and Wilkinson[28] have shown that the ketyl $(C_6H_5)_2\overset{\bullet}{C}-OH$ has a pK_a of 9.2, which makes it six units, at least, more acidic than the parent compound benzhydrol. That is, ketyl radical-anions are very much more stable with respect to the neutral molecules than are the alkoxide ions ($K_1 \gg K_2$).

$$R_2\overset{\bullet}{C}OH \overset{K_1}{\rightleftharpoons} R_2\overset{\bullet}{C}-O^- + H^+$$

$$R_2CHOH \overset{K_2}{\rightleftharpoons} R_2CHO^- + H^+$$

28. G. Porter and F. Wilkinson, *Trans. Faraday Soc.*, **57**, 1686 (1961).

If this is so,[28] then the effect of charge on the reaction rate is explicable. Assuming the transition state is similar to products, there will be a smaller energy barrier for conversion of R_2CHO^- to $R_2\overset{.}{C}$—O^- than for conversion of R_2CHOH to $R_2\overset{.}{C}$—OH. Second, recent evidence suggests that the oxidation of the formate-ion–cobalt(III) complex by permanganate takes place by a hydrogen-atom abstraction mechanism (page 72) and it is significant that there are many points of similarity between the ordinary permanganate-formate reaction and the permanganate-alkoxide reaction. Hydrogen-atom abstraction appears, in fact, to be the most satisfactory mechanism that one can write for the alcohol-permanganate reaction.[29] This type of mechanism is considered further in the sections that follow dealing with fluoral hydrate and formic acid oxidation.

FLUORAL HYDRATE

Fluoral (trifluoroacetaldehyde) exists in aqueous solution almost completely as the hydrate as a consequence of the strongly electron-withdrawing power of the trifluoromethyl group [structure (II)]. It is, therefore, a close analog of the secondary alcohols discussed in the previous section.

$$
\begin{array}{c}
\text{OH} \\
| \\
CF_3\text{---}C\text{---}Z \\
| \\
\text{H}
\end{array}
\qquad
\begin{array}{l}
Z = \text{R or Ar for secondary alcohol} \\
 = \text{O H for aldehyde hydrate}
\end{array}
$$

(II)

The permanganate oxidation of fluoral to trifluoroacetic acid has been examined over a very wide range of acidity and basicity with the result shown in Figure 2.[30]

In basic solution, the effect on the oxidation rate of the presence of two ionizing hydroxyls is clearly seen. The pK for the first ionization of fluoral hydrate is 10.0, and this clearly corresponds to the pH at the midpoint of the first curve. The second pK is not known, but dibasic acids, in which both hydroxyls are attached to the same atom, usually have their pKs about five units apart. On this basis, the midpoint of the

29. The similarity in the magnitude of the isotope effects for these reactions and for a known hydrogen-atom abstraction mechanism has been previously commented upon (page 16).
30. R. Stewart and M. Mocek, *Can. J. Chem.*, **41**, 1160 (1963).

second ionization should be at pH 15. The simplest analysis of the results in Figure 2, then, is that the dianion

$$CF_3—\overset{\displaystyle O^-}{\underset{\displaystyle O_-}{\overset{\displaystyle |}{\underset{\displaystyle |}{C}}}}—H$$

is oxidized by permanganate much more rapidly than is the monoanion

$$CF_3—\overset{\displaystyle O^-}{\underset{\displaystyle OH}{\overset{\displaystyle |}{\underset{\displaystyle |}{C}}}}—H$$

The rate law for the reaction in solutions more alkaline than pH 12 can be expressed as in Eq. (5).

$$v = k\left[CF_3—\overset{O^-}{\underset{O_-}{\overset{|}{\underset{|}{C}}}}—H\right][MnO_4^-] = k'\left[CF_3—\overset{OH}{\underset{OH}{\overset{|}{\underset{|}{C}}}}—H\right][MnO_4^-][OH^-]^2 \quad (5)$$

The rate of oxidation of fluoral by permanganate in neutral and dilute acid solution is slow because of the low concentration of the fluoral anions, which are the reactive species. Even at pH 6 the reaction rate is almost entirely due to the 0.02 per cent anion present at equilibrium. There is some indication of a reaction involving the neutral fluoral molecule and permanganate ion at pH 2, but the rate is so slow that one cannot be sure that some induced decomposition of permanganate is not occurring. In strongly acid solution, the reaction rate increases again because of formation of permanganic acid, a stronger oxidant.

The isotope effect for the oxidation of $CF_3CD(OH)_2$ shows a marked variation with acidity, or, more precisely, with the ionic state of the oxidant and reductant (Table 5-1).

The effect of ionic charge on the rate of reaction of the various Mn^{VII} and fluoral hydrate species is interesting. Interionic repulsions between similarly charged ions seem to play a minor role; that is, reducing the negative charge from 2 to 1 to 0 on the fluoral slows the rate of oxidation drastically, despite the fact that the oxidant is also an anion. On the other hand, reducing the negative charge from 1 to 0 on the oxidant causes a large increase in rate, but under these conditions the

Table 5-1 *Effect of state of ionization on the reaction of fluoral and permanganate*

Reductant	Oxidant	pH range where dominant	k_H, liter mole^{-1} sec^{-1}	k_H/k_D	$\Delta H^{\ddagger}$, kcal mole^{-1}
CF_3—C—H, with O^- above and O_- below	MnO_4^-	11	Very fast	5	7.5[a]
CF_3—C—H, with OH above and O_- below	MnO_4^-	5–10	1.3	14	12.4
CF_3—C—H, with OH above and OH below	MnO_4^-	~2	10^{-5}		
CF_3—C—H, with OH above and OH below	$HMnO_4$	$H_0 < -3$	Very fast	6	12.9[a]

[a] Includes preequilibrium step.

reductant has already become a neutral species. Thus, the bigger the negative charge on the reductant, the faster the reaction proceeds regardless of the charge on the oxidant.

It is worth comparing the data for the oxidation of all the trifluoromethylcarbinyl oxide ions by permanganate ion to see if a coherent picture of the mechanism emerges (Table 5-2).

The greatly accelerated rate of oxidation of $CF_3CHO_2^=$ suggests that a hydride ion is being removed by the oxidant. However, the rather small rate differences when $Z = H$, OH, and CF_3 are again more in accord with a hydrogen-atom abstraction mechanism. The increased rate when $Z = C_6H_5$ and the still greater effect of two phenyls (i.e., for the oxidation

$$O^-$$

Table 5-2 *Oxidation of* $CF_3-\overset{\displaystyle O^-}{\underset{\displaystyle H}{C}}-Z$ *by* MnO_4^-

Z	Relative rate
—O⁻	Very fast
—C_6H_5	6.5
—OH	1.1
—H	1.0
—CF_3	0.3

of benzhydrylate ion) would be in agreement with both hydride and hydrogen-atom mechanisms, since aromatic rings will tend to stabilize both products [Eq. (6)]. However, it will be recalled that substituents in the ring had a negligible effect on the reaction rate, and this is in support of the hydrogen-atom abstraction mechanism discussed earlier.

$$(6)$$

FORMIC ACID

The oxidation of formic acid to carbon dioxide by permanganate has been examined over a very wide range of acidities,[31-34] and the general characteristics of the reaction bear a striking resemblance to those for the

31. D. R. Mann and F. C. Tompkins, *Trans. Faraday Soc.*, **37**, 201 (1941).
32. L. M. Hill and F. C. Tompkins, *Trans. Roy. Soc. S. Africa*, **29**, 309 (1942).
33. K. B. Wiberg and R. Stewart, *J. Am. Chem. Soc.*, **78**, 1214 (1956).
34. J. Halpern and S. M. Taylor, *Discussions Faraday Soc.*, **1960**, 174.

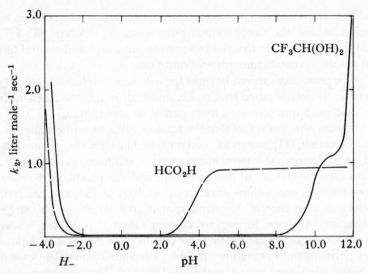

Figure 2   *The rate of permanganate oxidation of fluoral hydrate and formic acid as a function of acidity.*

aldehyde hydrates and alcohols discussed previously; that is, the anion is oxidized much faster than is the neutral molecule in the dilute aqueous region, but, in concentrated acid, the oxidation again becomes exceedingly fast (Figure 2).

The oxidation of formate ion by permanganate ion is the dominant reaction over almost the entire range of dilute aqueous solution. A simple hydride-ion shift from formate ion to permanganate has often been suggested as a likely path.

$$^-O_2C \overset{\frown}{\quad} H \quad MnO_4^- \rightarrow O_2C + HMnO_4^=$$

It has been observed, however, that the carbon dioxide formed in neutral solution when permanganate-^{18}O is the oxidant contains some oxygen-^{18}O.[33] It may be that an intermediate is formed that reacts by some oxygen-transfer route, and this possibility is considered in the discussion of the hydrogen-atom abstraction mechanism below.

Under neutral conditions, the un-ionized formic acid molecule seems to be completely unreactive to permanganate. However, at moderately high acidities, a slow reaction path involving neutral formic acid and permanganate ion can be observed.[34] Curiously enough, this reaction shows a small or zero kinetic isotope effect when DCO_2H is oxidized. In more concentrated sulfuric acid solution, the reaction again accelerates and the isotope effect returns ($k_H/k_D = 4.0$ in 38 per cent H_2SO_4). It is believed that neutral permanganic acid and neutral formic acid are the reactants under these conditions.[21]

The permanganate oxidation of formate ion complexed to cobalt(III) has recently been studied by Candlin and Halpern;[35] the mechanism of this reaction appears to be a hydrogen-atom abstraction. The evidence for this comes from the fact that the reaction takes two different paths; in one, the cobalt(III) acts as an oxidant together with the permanganate, and, in the other, the permanganate alone oxidizes the formate. The kinetics are first-order in permanganate and the complex; the reaction shows a deuterium-isotope effect of about 10:1 at $25°$; and the ratio of products is a function of the permanganate concentration. This suggests that an intermediate, formed by a 1-equivalent step, undergoes either internal oxidation-reduction forming cobalt(II) and carbon dioxide or, if more permanganate is readily available, a second 1-equivalent oxidation of the organic ligand to carbon dioxide [Eq. (7)]. The intermediate must

$$(NH_3)_5Co^{III}(HCO_2{}^-) + MnO_4{}^- \rightarrow [(NH_3)_5Co^{III}(CO_2{}^{\cdot-})] + HMnO_4{}^-$$

$$Co^{++} + CO_2 \qquad [(NH_3)_5Co^{III}H_2O] + CO_2 + Mn^{VI} \qquad (7)$$

be formed by hydrogen-atom abstraction by permanganate. The reaction rate and activation parameters are rather similar to those of the normal formate-permanganate reaction, and it may be that the latter also occurs by hydrogen-atom abstraction.

$$^-O_2CH + MnO_4{}^- \xrightarrow{\text{slow}} CO_2{}^{\cdot-} + HMnO_4{}^-$$

$$CO_2{}^{\cdot-} + MnO_4{}^- \xrightarrow{\text{fast}} CO_2 + MnO_4{}^=$$

The partial oxygen transfer that accompanies this reaction might result from the combination of the radical anion $CO_2{}^{\cdot-}$ with the paramagnetic ion $MnO_4{}^-$ to form an ester that could cleave to produce carbonate containing oxygen that was originally bonded to permanganate.

$$CO_2{}^{\cdot-} + MnO_4{}^- \rightarrow O_2C{-}O{-}MnO_3{}^= \longrightarrow CO_3{}^= + MnO_3$$
$$\longrightarrow CO_2 + MnO_4{}^=$$

35. J. P. Candlin and J. Halpern, *J. Am. Chem. Soc.*, **85**, 2518 (1963).

The similarities between the permanganate oxidation of alcohols, fluoro aldehyde hydrates, and formic acid have been referred to earlier (page 67). It appears that a hydrogen-atom abstraction from the anions of these molecules accounts most satisfactorily for the reaction mechanism in each case.

ALDEHYDES

The oxidation of aromatic aldehydes by permanganate in the neutral aqueous region has the stoichiometry shown in Eq. (8). The salient

$$3 \, \text{Z—C}_6\text{H}_4\text{—C}^{O}_{H} + 2\text{MnO}_4^- + \text{OH}^- \rightarrow 3 \, \text{Z—C}_6\text{H}_4\text{—CO}_2^- + 2\text{MnO}_2 + 2\text{H}_2\text{O} \quad (8)$$

features of the reaction mechanism may be summarized as follows:

1. The reaction is first order in both aldehyde and permanganate.
2. The aldehyde hydrogen is removed in the rate-controlling step (the deuterium-isotope effect is 7:1).
3. The reaction is subject to general acid catalysis.
4. Oxygen is transferred from permanganate to the reductant (^{18}O is found in the product, benzoic acid, when $\text{KMn}^{18}\text{O}_4$ is the oxidant).
5. Substituents in the aromatic ring have only a small effect on the rate (the Hammett rho value is -0.25).[36]

$$\text{ArC}^{O}_{H} + \text{MnO}_4^- + \text{H}^+ \rightleftharpoons \text{Ar—}\overset{\text{OH}}{\underset{H}{C}}\text{—OMnO}_3$$

$$\qquad\qquad (9)$$

$$\text{Ar—}\overset{\text{OH}}{\underset{\underset{B:}{H}}{C}}\text{—O—MnO}_3 \rightarrow \text{ArCO}_2\text{H} + \text{BH}^+ + \text{MnO}_3^-$$

The mechanism[36] suggested is the one shown in Eqs. (9). The intermediate ester

$$\text{Ar—}\overset{\text{OH}}{\underset{H}{C}}\text{—OMnO}_3$$

36. K. B. Wiberg and R. Stewart, *J. Am. Chem. Soc.*, **77**, 1786 (1955).

is presumed to be in rapid equilibrium with aldehyde and permanganate. The rate-controlling step is then the abstraction by base of the aldehyde proton and the concomitant scission of the oxygen-manganese bond. The general acid catalysis results from the fact that the base, designated B: in Eqs. (9), can be the anion of the weak acid used as buffer in the system. The relative insensitivity of the reaction to ring substituents, however, casts some doubt on this mechanism in view of the arguments presented about the rho value of the chromium(VI)-alcohol reaction (page 39).

When benzaldehyde is oxidized by permanganate in solutions much more acidic than pH 5, an autocatalytic reaction is observed. This is probably connected with the formation in acid solution of active manganese intermediates, such as Mn^{III}.

The mechanism of the permanganate oxidation of aromatic aldehydes in alkaline solution is more of an enigma. Benzaldehyde and most of its derivatives are oxidized much faster here than in neutral solution. This is particularly evident for aldehydes with electron withdrawing groups in the rings, since the Hammett rho value is now large and negative (-1.83 at pH 12.6). This means that even dilute solutions of p-nitrobenzaldehyde are oxidized by permanganate in only a few seconds in alkaline solution. On the other hand, p-tolualdehyde is oxidized much more slowly and, in fact, at about the same rate as in neutral solution.

The most attractive mechanism for the alkaline permanganate–aldehyde reaction is a variation of one suggested by Tompkins[37] in which the aldehyde molecule adds OH^- to form the ion

$$
\begin{array}{c}
O^- \\
| \\
Ar—C—H \\
| \\
OH
\end{array}
$$

which can then lose a hydrogen to permanganate. This would then be a close analog of the reaction of aldehyde hydrates and alcohols discussed earlier. The reaction appears to be more complex than this, however, since the kinetics are less than first-order in hydroxyl ion, and the reaction shows a number of other anomalies. Perhaps the most striking feature is the almost identical rates found for the oxidation of the series of aromatic aldehydes by permanganate and manganate ions.[36] In all other cases studied, manganate oxidations are much slower than those of permanganate. This suggests that the rate-controlling step might

37. F. C. Tompkins, *Trans. Faraday Soc.*, **39**, 280 (1943).

precede the entry of the oxidant into the mechanism, but the kinetics themselves do not support this idea. Radicals have been suggested as possible reaction intermediates, but, clearly, more work is required to elucidate the mechanism of the alkaline permanganate oxidation of aldehydes.

PHENOLS

Although the kinetics of the reaction of permanganate with phenols was a matter of some interest during the 1930s, little information on mechanism was obtained. This is because phenols, on oxidation, undergo complete disruption of the molecule, and, if sufficient oxidant is present they are degraded to carbon dioxide. Hinshelwood et al.,[38, 39] showed that the first oxidation reaction was the slow step, which was followed by rapid degradation of the ring, but the catastrophic fate of the phenol molecule makes it difficult to determine the exact nature of this first step.

Alexander and Tompkins[40] showed that the rate of oxidation of 2,6-dinitrophenol was accelerated by added manganous ions and inhibited by added fluoride ions. This, as we have seen, is an indication that manganese ions of intermediate valence are the active oxidants. They suggested that hydroxyl radicals generated by the action of Mn^{III} and Mn^{IV} on water were the active oxidants.

$$Mn^{IV} + H_2O \rightarrow Mn^{III} + H^+ + HO \cdot$$

Electron-withdrawing groups in the aromatic ring tend to stabilize the phenol to permanganate oxidation. Phenol itself, mononitrophenols, and hydroxybenzoic acids are completely and virtually instantaneously oxidized by permanganate in dilute acid. The oxidation of di- and tri-nitrophenols is slow enough to be measured. The enthalpies of activation of a series of polynitrophenols vary from 11.6 kcal mole^{-1} for picric acid to 15.0 kcal mole^{-1} for 2,6-dinitrophenol.[39] Correlations of activation parameters with structure are very difficult, however, because of the varying acidities of the phenols. That is, the oxidized species appears to be the anion for picric acid but is probably the neutral molecule for 2,6-dinitrophenol.

38. C. N. Hinshelwood, *Trans. Chem. Soc.*, **1919**, 1180.
39. C. N. Hinshelwood and C. A. Winkler, *J. Chem. Soc.*, **1936**, 368.
40. E. A. Alexander and F. C. Tompkins, *Trans. Faraday Soc.*, 35, 1156 (1939).

OXALIC ACID

Although the oxidation of oxalic acid by permanganate in acid solution has been the subject of discussion for almost 100 years, its mechanism is still not completely understood. The manganese undergoes a change of five oxidation units in this reaction, ending up as manganous ion.

$$2MnO_4^- + 5H_2C_2O_4 + 6H^+ \rightarrow 2Mn^{++} + 10CO_2 + 8H_2O$$

The autocatalytic nature of this reaction is well known and is caused by the accumulation of manganous ions in solution. Addition of the manganous salts at the beginning of the reaction eliminates the induction period, whereas addition of fluoride ion can inhibit the reaction almost indefinitely by complexing with the active species, manganese(III).

The extensive work on this complex reaction by many investigators over the years has been reviewed by Ladbury and Cullis,[2] and it will not be repeated here. The most recent work on the mechanism has been done by Adler and Noyes,[41] who suggest the following reaction path. The reaction is initiated by the oxidation of a manganese(II)-oxalate complex by permanganate. (Manganese-oxalate complexes are known to exist.)

$$MnO_4^- + MnC_2O_4 \rightarrow MnO_4^= + MnC_2O_4^+$$

If manganous ion is present in sufficient concentration, the following steps then occur:

$$Mn^{VI} + Mn^{II} \rightarrow 2Mn^{IV}$$

$$Mn^{IV} + Mn^{II} \rightarrow 2Mn^{III}$$

The manganese(III) complexes decompose in subsequent steps.

41. S. J. Adler and R. M. Noyes, *J. Am. Chem. Soc.*, **77**, 2036 (1955).

chapter | # Other Transition
six | # Metal Oxidants

A wide variation exists in both the reactivity of transition metal oxidants and the type of reaction that they undergo. The oxidation-reduction potentials give only a very rough measure of their reactivities. Mechanistic features rather than the free energy difference between oxidant and its reduced form (oxidation-reduction potential) are the critical factors in many of the reactions discussed in these, as in earlier, sections.

PERVANADYL ION

Pentavalent vanadium in acid solution exists as the yellow pervanadyl ion VO_2^+. The recent extensive work of Waters and his group has shown this reagent to be a versatile oxidant, the reduction product being the blue tetravalent vanadyl ion VO^{++}. The polymerization of added olefins, which accompanies these reactions, suggests that it is a 1-equivalent oxidant that produces organic radicals as reaction intermediates.

The oxidation of cyclohexanol to the ketone by VO_2^+ in acid solution undoubtedly proceeds via the red complex which forms immediately upon the addition of pervanadyl ion to the alcohol in aqueous acid. The decomposition of the complex is rate-controlling, as shown by the existence of an isotope effect in the oxidation of cyclohexanol-1-d. The concomitant polymerization of added acrylonitrile indicates a homolytic scission like that shown in Eqs. (1)–(3).[1] A decomposition of the

1. J. S. Littler and W. A. Waters, *J. Chem. Soc.*, **1959**, 4046.

vanadate-ester intermediate by what could be called the Westheimer chromate-ester mechanism (page 37) is considered unlikely by Littler and Waters because of the polymerization evidence, and because they have shown that cyclohexyl vanadate is not readily decomposed to ketone by acids or bases.

$$VO_2^+ + H_3O^+ + \text{(cyclohexyl-OH,D)} \rightleftharpoons \text{(cyclohexyl-O-V(OH)_3^+,D)} \qquad (1)$$

$$\text{(cyclohexyl-O-V(OH)_3^+,D)} \xrightarrow{\text{slow}} \text{(cyclohexenyl-O-V(OH)_2^+)} + DOH \qquad (2)$$

$$\text{(cyclohexenyl-O-V(OH)_2^+)} + VO_2^+ \xrightarrow{\text{fast}} \text{(cyclohexanone)} {=} O + 2V^{IV} \qquad (3)$$

In the presence of small amounts of bromide ion the oxidation of alcohols takes a different course. The principal reaction is now zero-order in alcohol, bromine atoms produced in the rate-controlling step being implicated as the active oxidants.[2]

$$V^V + Br^- \rightarrow V^{IV} + Br\cdot$$

$$R_2CHOH + Br\cdot \rightarrow R_2\overset{\cdot}{C}OH + Br^- + H^+$$

With certain alcohols, the decomposition of the vanadium(V)-alcohol complex does not involve C—H bond rupture. Thus, t-butyl phenyl carbinol gives on oxidation a fair yield of benzaldehyde. The formation of the fairly stable t-butyl radical undoubtedly aids the C—C bond scission, and this reaction [Eq. (4)] may, indeed, accompany the homolytic cleavage of the metal-oxygen bond.[3]

$$\underset{C_6H_5\overset{|}{C}Ht\text{-}Bu}{\overset{OH}{}} \xrightarrow{V^V} \left[\underset{C_6H_5\overset{|}{C}Ht\text{-}Bu}{\overset{O\cdot}{}} \right] \rightarrow$$

$$C_6H_5CHO + t\text{-}Bu\cdot \rightarrow C_6H_5CHO + t\text{-}BuOH \qquad (4)$$

2. K. Julian and W. A. Waters, *J. Chem. Soc.*, **1962**, 818.
3. J. R. Jones and W. A. Waters, *J. Chem. Soc.*, **1960**, 2772.

Ketones with α-hydrogens are readily oxidized by pervanadyl ion, and again the mechanism is believed to be the homolytic decomposition of a cyclic complex to give intermediate radicals.[4] A sizable isotope effect ($k_H/k_D = 4.2$ at 50°) is found for the oxidation of cyclohexanone. This mechanism, shown in Eq. (5), is analogous to that proposed for the selenium dioxide oxidation of ketones (page 107).

$$\rightarrow \text{further degradation} \qquad (5)$$

Glycols are cleaved readily by vanadium(V), but only if a ketone can be produced by the cleavage.[5] Primary and secondary diols tend to give the ordinary products of alcohol oxidation, that is, 2,3-butandiol

faster than

$$(6)$$

gives 2,3-butandione. It is especially interesting that the cleavage of pinacol to give 2 moles of acetone is actually faster than the diol reaction [Eqs. (6)].[6] This behavior distinguishes vanadium(V) from the other

4. J. S. Littler, *J. Chem. Soc.*, **1962**, 832.
5. See D. M. West and D. A. Skoog, *J. Am. Chem. Soc.*, **82**, 280 (1960).
6. J. S. Littler, A. I. Mallet, and W. A. Waters, *J. Chem. Soc.*, **1960**, 2761.

glycol-cleaving reagents (Chapter 7), which are, in fact, 2-equivalent oxidants. The homolytic decomposition of a chelate complex is believed to be the reaction mechanism [Eq. (7)].

$$
\begin{array}{c}
CH_3 \\
\,|\;\; H \\
CH_3-C-O \\
\,| \\
CH_3-C-O \\
\,|\;\; H \\
CH_3
\end{array}
\!\!\! VO_2^+ \rightarrow
\begin{array}{c}
CH_3 \\
\,| \\
CH_3-C\!\!=\!\!O \\
\\
CH_3-\overset{\cdot}{C}-OH \\
\,| \\
CH_3
\end{array}
+ V^{IV}
\tag{7}
$$

COBALT(III) AND CERIUM(IV)

These powerful oxidants normally behave as 1-equivalent reagents. The oxidation-reduction potentials are 1.8 volts for the Co^{3+}-Co^{++} couple and 1.6 volts for the Ce^{4+}-Ce^{3+} couple. Cobaltic ion, indeed, can oxidize water, generating hydroxyl radicals.[7]

The oxidation of alcohols by Co^{III} occurs more readily than that of ketones. (The reverse is true for V^V and Ce^{IV}).[8, 9] The rate of the facile alcohol oxidation is inversely proportional to the hydrogen-ion concentration and exhibits an isotope effect when the alcohol carbon is substituted by deuterium.[9] The isotope effect is small, $k_H/k_D = 1.7$ at 10° for the Co^{III}–cyclohexanol-1-d reaction, but this is not surprising considering the reactivity of cobaltic ion. It is believed that the rapid exchange of a ligand with an alcohol molecule occurs with the ion $Co(OH)(H_2O)_5^{++}$ but not with the ion $Co(H_2O)_6^{3+}$, accounting for the inverse acid dependence [Eq. (8)]. Hoare and Waters believe the complex decomposes to a

$$
Co(H_2O)_6^{+3} \rightleftharpoons Co(OH)(H_2O)_5^{++} + H^+
\tag{8}
$$

radical, which is in turn rapidly oxidized.[9] [Eq. (9).] The much slower degradation of t-butyl alcohol by cobaltic ion probably generates t-butoxy radicals.

$$
Co^{III}-O-\overset{\displaystyle H}{\underset{\displaystyle R}{C}}-R \rightarrow
\left[Co\text{---}O\diagdown\!\!\diagup C\overset{R}{\diagdown R} \right]
\rightarrow Co^{II} + HO-\overset{R}{\underset{\cdot\;\diagdown R}{C}}
\tag{9}
$$

The cobaltic ion oxidation of ketones in acid solution produces extensive decomposition of the organic molecule. The oxidation rate is about 300 times faster than the enolization rate for the ketone, and the

7. C. E. H. Bawn and A. G. White, *J. Chem. Soc.*, **1951**, 331.
8. D. G. Hoare and W. A. Waters, *J. Chem. Soc.*, **1962**, 971.
9. D. G. Hoare and W. A. Waters, *J. Chem. Soc.*, **1962**, 965.

enol form is clearly not involved here.[8] The absence of an isotope effect
in the oxidation of $(CH_3CD_2)_2C\!=\!\!O$ suggests that the rate-controlling
step is either complex formation or electron abstraction by cobaltic ion,
possibly after formation of Co^{III}-ketone complex.

Ceric ion degrades ketones rapidly in acid solution at a rate considerably greater than the enolization rate of the ketone. Complex
formation immediately occurs when ceric ion and acetone are mixed,[10]
and the rate-controlling step is decomposition of this complex to produce
cerous ion and a ketone radical, which undergoes further fast
decomposition.

$$Ce^{IV} + (CH_3)_2C\!=\!\!O \rightarrow Ce\!-\!\!-O\!=\!\!C(CH_3)_2 \rightarrow Ce^{III} + radicals$$

Ceric ion–alcohol complex formation also precedes the slower oxidation
of alcohols by this reagent. The kinetics of the oxidation of formaldehyde
by ceric ion in acid solution have been examined and the mechanism in
Eqs. (10) suggested.[11, 12] Complex formation may occur here also.

$$Ce^{IV} + CH_2(OH)_2 \rightarrow Ce^{III} + CH_2\!\!\underset{OH}{\overset{O\cdot}{<}} + H^+ \qquad \text{rate-controlling}$$

$$(10)$$

$$CH_2\!\!\underset{OH}{\overset{O\cdot}{<}} + Ce^{IV} \rightarrow HCO_2H + Ce^{III} \qquad \text{fast}$$

THALLIUM(III) AND MERCURY(II)

These reagents are normally 2-equivalent oxidants, thallium(I) and
mercury(0) being the initial reduction products.[13] Mercury(I) is
formed by reaction of mercury(0) and mercury(II). The oxidative
degradation of enolizable ketones by these reagents proceeds via the
enol, and the rate-controlling step is, in fact, enolization. Similar rates
are observed for the oxidation of cyclohexanone by the 2-equivalent
reagents Tl^{III}, Hg^{II}, Mn^{VII}, as for the halogenation of this ketone by
bromine and iodine. In all cases the reaction is zero-order in the
inorganic reagent.[14]

10. S. Venkatakrishnan and M. Santappa, *Z. Physik. Chem. (Frankfurt)*, **16**,
    73 (1958).
11. G. Hargreaves and L. H. Sutcliffe, *Trans. Faraday Soc.*, **51**, 1105 (1955).
12. See also C. G. Swain and K. Hedberg, *J. Am. Chem. Soc.*, **72**, 3373 (1950).
13. A. M. Armstrong and J. Halpern, *Can. J. Chem.*, **35**, 1020 (1957).
14. J. S. Littler, *J. Chem. Soc.*, **1962**, 827.

Many reactions of organic mercury compounds might be classed as oxidation reactions,[15-17] but it does not seem appropriate to attempt to treat them here.

COPPER(II)

One of the most frequently used oxidants in the organic laboratory is Fehling's solution—an alkaline cupric solution containing tartrate to complex with the copper ion and prevent precipitation of the hydroxide. Aliphatic aldehydes and carbohydrates with "free" carbonyl groups are rapidly oxidized by this reagent.[18] It is used chiefly to test for the presence of such groups, since the yields of acid obtained by the action of Fehling's solution on aldehydes are usually poor. The attention is thus focused on the inorganic product in the reaction—the red cuprous oxide precipitate that indicates oxidation has occurred. Copper(II) tends to react in 1-equivalent steps, and the extensive degradation accompanying Fehling's solution oxidations is doubtless caused by generation of transient radicals during the oxidation.

Cupric ion has proved to be an excellent reagent for the oxidative coupling of acetylenes, the reactions usually being conducted in pyridine or other amine solution.[19, 20]

$$2RC\equiv CH + 2Cu^{++} + 2C_5H_5N \rightarrow RC\equiv C-C\equiv CR + 2C_5H_5NH^+ + 2Cu^+$$

A study of the mechanism of this reaction by Klebanski et al.[21] indicates that the formation of the carbanion is rate-determining. The role of cupric ion appears to be twofold: It is the oxidant that generates the coupling radicals, and it aids in the formation of the carbanion by complexing with acetylide.

$$RC\equiv CH \xrightarrow[\text{base}]{Cu^{++}} RC\equiv C^- + H^+$$

$$RC\equiv C^- + Cu^{++} \longrightarrow RC\equiv C\cdot + Cu^+$$

$$2RC\equiv C\cdot \longrightarrow RC\equiv C-C\equiv CR$$

15. J. Chatt, *Chem. Revs.*, **48**, 7 (1951).
16. J. H. Robson and G. F. Wright, *Can. J. Chem.*, **38**, 21 (1960).
17. F. R. Jensen and R. J. Ouellette, *J. Am. Chem. Soc.*, **83**, 4477 (1961).
18. As they are with Tollen's reagent, ammonia-complexed silver ion; the properties of Ag^+ and Cu^{++} as oxidants are rather similar. See, for example, A. H. Webster and J. Halpern, *J. Phys. Chem.*, **61**, 1239 (1957).
19. G. Eglinton and A. R. Galbraith, *Chem. & Ind. (London)*, **1956**, 737.
20. F. Toda and M. Nakagawa, *Bull. Chem. Soc. Japan*, **33**, 223 (1960).
21. A. L. Klebanski, O. V. Grachev, and O. M. Kuznetsova, *J. Gen. Chem. (U.S.S.R.)*, **27**, 2977 (1957).

Variations of this reaction include the coupling of acetylenes by the use of cuprous ion and oxygen, the coupling of an acetylene and an ethynyl halide by the use of cuprous ion, and even the oxidative coupling of acetylides by permanganate.[22]

The copper salt–catalyzed reaction of olefins with peresters is an interesting example of the operation of the 1-equivalent cuprous-cupric couple.[23] t-Butyl perbenzoate when heated with 1-butene and a catalytic amount of cuprous bromide produces chiefly 3-benzoyloxy-1-butene (together with some 1-benzoyloxy-2-butene).

$$C_6H_5CO_3t\text{-Bu} + CH_3CH_2CH{=}CH_2 \xrightarrow{Cu^+} CH_3\underset{\underset{O_2CC_6H_5}{|}}{C}HCH{=}CH_2 + t\text{-BuOH}$$

The mechanism of this reaction appears to be the following:[24]

$$C_6H_5CO_3t\text{-Bu} + Cu^I \rightarrow C_6H_5CO_2Cu^{II} + t\text{-BuO·}$$

$$t\text{-BuO·} + CH_3CH_2CH{=}CH_2 \rightarrow t\text{-BuOH} + CH_3\overset{·}{C}HCH{=}CH_2$$

$$CH_3\overset{·}{C}HCH{=}CH_2 + C_6H_5CO_2Cu^{II} \rightarrow CH_3\underset{\underset{O_2CC_6H_5}{|}}{C}HCH{=}CH_2 + Cu^I$$

The mesomeric butenyl radical can also react at the 1-carbon to produce the minor oxidation product. The transfer of carboxylate from Cu^{II} to butenyl [Eq. (11)] is analogous to the carboxylate transfers from Co^{III} to Cr^{II} discussed in a later section.[25]

$$(11)$$

22. H. H. Schlubach and V. Wolf, *Ann.*, **568**, 141 (1950).
23. M. S. Kharasch and A. Fono, *J. Org. Chem.*, **24**, 606 (1959).
24. J. K. Kochi, *J. Am. Chem. Soc.*, **84**, 774, 1572 (1962).
25. The question of electron- and ligand-transfer mechanisms in the oxidation of organic radicals by metal ions is being studied by Kochi et al.; see, J. K. Kochi and F. F. Rust, *J. Am. Chem. Soc.*, **84**, 3946 (1962), and references therein. See also C. Bamford, A. Jenkins, and R. Johnston, *Proc. Roy. Soc. (London)*, **239A**, 214 (1957).

OSMIUM TETROXIDE

The elegant and well-known work of Criegee[26, 27] on the oxidation of alkenes to glycols with osmium tetroxide showed that cis dihydroxylation occurs and established Eq. (12) as the course of the reaction.

$$
\begin{array}{ccccc}
RCH & & RCHO & & RCHOH \\
\| & + OsO_4 \longrightarrow & | \quad \rangle OsO_2 \xrightarrow{H_2O} & | & + H_2OsO_4 \quad (12) \\
RCH & & RCHO & & RCHOH
\end{array}
$$

If the reaction is conducted in a nonhydroxylic solvent, an intermediate complex, believed to be the osmate ester, can be isolated and then hydrolyzed to the glycol in a separate step. Hydrolytic cleavage presumably occurs at the osmium-oxygen bonds in view of the stereospecificity of the reaction.

Traces of osmium tetroxide have been used with other strong oxidants in many alkene oxidations.[28-30] In these cases, it is believed that the role of the osmium tetroxide is that shown in Eq. (12).

The mechanism of ruthenium tetroxide oxidations appears to be somewhat different from that of osmium tetroxide.[31]

FERRICYANIDE

Potassium ferricyanide can best be described as a 1-equivalent electron-abstracting reagent.[32] The polarizable cyano ligands around the central atom in ferricyanide facilitate electron transfer from electron-rich substrates to the iron. Phenols are oxidized to various, often complex,

$$(13)$$

26. R. Criegee, *Ann.*, **522**, 75 (1936).
27. R. Criegee, B. Marchand, and H. Wannowius, *Ann.*, **550**, 99 (1942).
28. K. A. Hofmann, *Ber.*, **45**, 3329 (1912).
29. M. Mugden and D. P. Young, *J. Chem. Soc.*, **1949**, 2988.
30. R. Pappo, D. S. Allen, Jr., R. U. Lemieux, and W. S. Johnson, *J. Org. Chem.*, **21**, 478 (1956).
31. C. Djerrasi and R. R. Engle, *J. Am. Chem. Soc.*, **75**, 3838 (1953).
32. B. S. Thyagarajan, *Chem. Revs.*, **58**, 439 (1958).

products via intermediate radicals. The greater oxidation rate in alkaline solution indicates that the phenoxide ion, not the phenol, is the electron donor [Eq. (13)]. As well as the ortho-coupled product shown in this equation, ortho-para and para-para coupling can occur, and in some cases very complex products are formed. Coupling does not occur when the radical is sufficiently stable, as in the case of 2,4,6-tri-t-butylphenoxyl [Eq. (14)].[33]

$$t\text{-Bu} \underset{t\text{-Bu}}{\overset{O^-}{\underset{}{\bigodot}}} t\text{-Bu} \quad \xrightarrow{\text{Fe(CN)}_6{}^{3-}} \quad t\text{-Bu} \underset{t\text{-Bu}}{\overset{O\cdot}{\underset{}{\bigodot}}} t\text{-Bu} \qquad (14)$$

Aldehydes, ketones, and nitroalkanes are also oxidized by alkaline ferricyanide, and the rate is proportional to the hydroxide-ion concentration.[34] Presumably, the enol anion, the analog of phenoxide ion, gives up an electron to the oxidant.

$$\underset{\text{RCH}_2\text{CR}}{\overset{O}{\parallel}} \xrightarrow{\text{OH}^-} \underset{\text{RCH=CR}}{\overset{O^-}{\mid}} \xrightarrow{\text{Fe(CN)}_6{}^{3-}} \left[\underset{\text{RCH=CR}}{\overset{O\cdot}{\mid}} \leftrightarrow \underset{\text{RĊHCR}}{\overset{O}{\parallel}} \right] \rightarrow \text{dimer}$$

Vinyl polymerization is not induced by these systems,[34] but this may be because the relatively stable enol radicals are not sufficiently reactive.

The ferricyanide oxidation of mercaptans produces disulfides.

$$2\text{RSH} + 2\text{Fe(CN)}_6{}^{3-} \rightarrow \text{RSSR} + 2\text{Fe(CN)}_6{}^{4-} + 2\text{H}^+$$

The rate of this reaction is proportional to the concentration of the anion RS$^-$ and is slowed by the presence of excess cyanide ion. In the presence of excess cyanide, the reaction is believed to be a simple electron abstraction from the mercaptide ion by the ferricyanide ion, followed by dimerization of the mercaptyl radical.[35]

$$\text{RS}^- + \text{Fe(CN)}_6{}^{3-} \rightarrow \text{RS}\cdot + \text{Fe(CN)}_6{}^{4-}$$

$$2\text{RS}\cdot \rightarrow \text{RSSR}$$

33. C. D. Cook and R. C. Woodworth, *J. Am. Chem. Soc.*, **75**, 6242 (1953).
34. P. T. Speakman and W. A. Waters, *J. Chem. Soc.*, **1955**, 40.
35. I. M. Kolthoff, E. J. Meehan, M. S. Tsao, and Q. W. Choi, *J. Phys. Chem.*, **66**, 1233 (1962).

In the absence of excess cyanide, the reaction is much faster and may involve a displacement of a cyanide ligand by the highly nucleophilic mercaptide ion.[35]

$$Fe(CN)_6{}^{3-} + RS^- \rightleftharpoons Fe(CN)_5SR^{3-} + CN^-$$

$$Fe(CN)_5SR^{3-} \xrightarrow{fast} Fe(CN)_5{}^{3-} + RS \cdot$$

$$Fe(CN)_5{}^{3-} + CN^- \xrightarrow{fast} Fe(CN)_6{}^{4-}$$

$$2RS \cdot \longrightarrow RSSR$$

PALLADIUM CHLORIDE

Although it has been known for a very long time that the salts of noble metals, such as platinum and palladium, could oxidize alkenes to aldehydes and ketones, it is only recently that the reaction has been intensively investigated.[36] The reaction has become, in fact, an extremely important industrial process, since it accomplishes the conversion of ethylene to acetaldehyde and of 1,2- and 2,3-olefins to methyl ketones in homogeneous aqueous solution at room temperature. If ethylene is passed through an aqueous solution of palladium chloride, the gas is absorbed, and finely divided palladium begins to precipitate.

$$CH_2{=}CH_2 + PdCl_2 + H_2O \rightarrow CH_3CHO + Pd + 2H\,Cl$$

$$CH_3CH_2CH{=}CH_2 + PdCl_2 + H_2O \rightarrow CH_3CH_2\overset{\displaystyle O}{\overset{\displaystyle \|}{C}}CH_3 + Pd + 2HCl$$

The palladium can be reoxidized by oxygen to the Pd^{II} for reuse.

It has been shown that the ethylene reaction does not proceed via hydration of the alkene to ethanol followed by oxidation to acetaldehyde, since ethanol is oxidized only very slowly under the reaction conditions. Neither does vinyl alcohol appear to be formed as an intermediate, since its rearrangement to acetaldehyde would involve proton exchange with the aqueous solvent, and it has been shown in at least one case that the four hydrogens in the ethylene are retained in the product. The reaction occurs in two stages, complex formation and complex hydrolysis.

$$C_2H_4 + PdCl_4{}^= \rightleftharpoons [C_2H_4PdCl_3]^- + Cl^-$$

$$[C_2H_4PdCl_3]^- + H_2O \rightarrow CH_3CHO + Pd + 2HCl + Cl^-$$

36. J. Smidt, *Chem. & Ind. (London)*, **1962**, 54, and references therein; J. Smidt and R. Sieber, *Angew. Chem.*, **71**, 626 (1959).

The hydrolysis of the complex to products is inhibited by acid but will nevertheless proceed at a reasonable rate in 0.1 N hydrochloric acid. The mechanism put forward by Smidt[36] involves a nucleophilic attack by hydroxide ion on one of the olefinic carbons with a simultaneous, 1,2-hydrogen shift and expulsion of the palladium with the pi electrons that bound the olefin to it [Eq. (15)]. There are several aspects of this mechanism that are not particularly attractive. First, it seems unlikely that the

$$\begin{array}{c} \underset{H}{\overset{H}{>}}C{=}C\underset{H}{\overset{H}{<}} + PdCl_4^= \rightleftharpoons \underset{H}{\overset{H}{>}}C{\doteq}C\underset{\underset{PdCl_3^-}{H}}{\overset{H}{<}} + Cl^- \end{array} \tag{15}$$

$$\underset{H}{\overset{H}{>}}C{\doteq}C\underset{\underset{PdCl_3^-}{H}}{\overset{H}{<}} + OH^- \rightarrow CH_3C\underset{H}{\overset{\overset{+}{O}H}{<}} + Pd + 3Cl^-$$

inhibition of the decomposition of the complex by acid can be caused by a decrease in the concentration of the nucleophile hydroxide ion. In 0.1 N acid, the hydroxide-ion concentration is only 10^{-13} M, and it seems certain that displacement by the nucleophile water would become the dominant path long before this acidity is reached. Second, the change of charge from plus to minus on an atom in a single step, as shown for oxygen in Eq. (15), is most unusual. The acid inhibition can hardly be caused by protonation of the palladium anion, since this should increase the rate of electron abstraction by the metal.

$$PdCl_4^= + C_2H_4 + H_2O \rightleftharpoons \left[\underset{H}{\overset{H}{>}}C{\doteq}C\underset{\underset{PdCl_2OH}{H}}{\overset{H}{<}} \right]^- + 2Cl^- + H^+$$

$$\underset{\underset{PdCl_2^-}{}}{\overset{H}{\underset{}{H{-}C{-}C{-}H}}}\overset{(H)}{} \quad \underset{H}{\overset{H}{>}} \rightarrow H{-}C{-}C\underset{H}{\overset{H}{<}}_{OH} + Pd + 2Cl^-$$
$$\overset{+}{\rightarrow} CH_3CHO + H^+ \tag{16}$$

A rearrangement of the pi complex to a sigma complex, accompanying proton abstraction from carbon, has been suggested by Moiseev, Vargaftik, and Syrkin as the mechanism.[37] This would result in vinyl

37. I. I. Moiseev, M. N. Vargaftik, and Y. K. Syrkin, *Doklady Akad. Nauk S.S.S.R.*, **130**, 820 (1960); **133**, 377 (1960).

alcohol formation, which, on the basis of present evidence, does not appear to be an intermediate. A variation of the Smidt mechanism [Eq. (16)], in which hydrolyzed π and σ complexes are formed,[38] is in agreement with the kinetic and tracer work but does not require hydroxyl ion to be a nucleophile in acid solution.

ORGANIC LIGANDS AND TRANSITION METAL OXIDANTS

The use of organic ligands in the study of certain inorganic oxidations has been cleverly exploited by Taube and his group. They have taken advantage of the fact that Cr^{III} (and Pt^{IV}) ligands do not exchange with the solvent or with ions in solution. They have shown that the oxidation of Cr^{II} to Cr^{III} by a reagent, such as $(NH_3)_5CoCl^{++}$, proceeds with transfer of chlorine from cobalt to chromium.[39] The term *inner sphere reaction* has been used to describe this 1-equivalent oxidation, whose net result is a transfer of a chlorine atom from oxidant to reductant. The 2-equivalent Pt^{II}-Pt^{IV} exchange is believed also to proceed via a chlorine-bridged complex.[40] This reaction results in a net transfer of chlorinium ion, Cl^+, from oxidant to reductant.[41]

38. This mechanism was suggested by Professor J. Halpern (personal communication), who pointed out the analogy of addition of Pd—OH across the C=C double bond with the well-known oxymercuration reaction.[15] In the latter case, the intermediate σ-complex is stable to oxidation—presumably because mercury(II) is a weaker oxidant than palladium(II).

39. H. Taube, *J. Am. Chem. Soc.*, **77**, 4481 (1955).

40. F. Basolo, M. Morrison, and R. G. Pearson, *Discussions Faraday Soc.*, **29**, 80 (1960).

41. Chlorinium transfer from chlorine to, say, phenol occurs in the electrophilic aromatic substitution reaction [Eq. (25)]. This does not necessarily mean that a free chlorinium ion is an intermediate in the reaction. Similarly, in the chloride-bridged Pt^{II}-Pt^{IV} reaction, if the chlorine is

$$Cl_2 + \text{(phenol)} \rightarrow \text{(intermediate)} + Cl^- \rightarrow \text{(chlorophenol)} + HCl \qquad (25)$$

considered to exist essentially as Cl^- in reactant, transition state, and product, the transfer of Cl^- from platinum(IV) to platinum(II) must be accompanied by the transfer of two electrons in the opposite direction. Although the vector sum of these processes is a Cl^+ transfer from platinum(IV) to platinum(II), the inorganic chemist may prefer to treat them as separate (though necessarily complementary) processes. See J. Halpern, *Quart. Revs. (London)*, **1961**, 207.

Some interesting results have been observed when carboxyl ligands of Co^{III} are transferred to Cr^{II}.[42] The bridging action of a carboxyl group reduces the electrostatic repulsion between the reacting cations and provides a convenient reaction path, since it allows substitution by Cr^{II} to occur on oxygen at an equivalent, conjugative position [Eq. (17)].

$$Co^{III}\!\!-\!\!O\diagdown\!\!\diagup O + Cr^{II} \rightarrow \left[Co\text{---}O\diagdown\!\!\diagup O\text{---}Cr \right] \rightarrow Co^{II} + O\diagdown\!\!\diagup O\!\!-\!\!Cr^{III}$$
$$\underset{R}{C} \qquad\qquad \underset{R}{C} \qquad\qquad \underset{R}{C} \qquad (17)$$

Except for the homolytic character of this reaction and the ionic character of the metal-oxygen bond it is similar, indeed, to the S_N2' solvolysis mechanism of allylic halides.[43] The latter, in their competition with the direct S_N2 displacement, do not possess the advantages shown in Eq. (17) of a greatly reduced repulsion between like-charged ions.

The formulas in the following equations are written as if the metal-carboxyl bonds are covalent. If the bonds are considered to be completely ionic, the bridging ligand can be thought of as an intermediary that donates and receives an electron (or vice versa) in successive reactions with the metal atoms to which it is coordinated.

(I)

(II)

When the group attached to the carboxyl ligand, R in Eq. (17), is itself a conjugating group [see structures (I) and (II)], then attack at a remote center can occur. Thus, fumarate, but not succinate, and terephthalate, but not isophthalate, allow attack at the remote carboxyl group, the further reduction in ion repulsion being reflected in increased reaction rates.[44, 45]

42. H. Taube, *Can. J. Chem.*, **37**, 129 (1959).
43. R. H. De Wolfe and W. G. Young, *Chem. Revs.*, **56**, 769 (1956).
44. D. K. Sebera and H. Taube, *J. Am. Chem. Soc.*, **83**, 1785 (1961).
45. R. T. M. Fraser and H. Taube, *J. Am. Chem. Soc.*, **81**, 5000 (1959).

Taube et al. have discovered that some interesting chemical changes occur in a conjugated organic group, like hydrogen maleate or methyl maleate, when it is the bridging ligand in the Co^{III}-Cr^{II} reaction. Extensive isomerization of maleate to the more stable isomer fumarate accompanies the transfer.[46]

The extent of the cis-trans isomerization that accompanies the oxidation is a linear function of the acidity of the medium: The higher the acidity the greater the isomerization. The presence of a first-order term in $[H^+]$ in the rate expression for those oxidations that proceed by bridged dicarboxyl intermediates is, in fact, an indication that attack at the remote carboxyl function is competing with the normal reaction at the near carboxyl.[46] Taube has suggested that the function of the extra proton is to promote conjugation in the bridging ligand.[42] With certain conjugated ligands, attack at the remote carboxyl can occur by three paths involving the neutral carboxyl group, the carboxylate anion, and a protonated carboxyl (not necessarily the remote one).

$$\tag{18}$$

Accompanying the isomerization of maleate to fumarate, which takes place in the bridged intermediate, is some exchange of the ethylenic hydrogens of the ligand with the solvent hydrogens. Solvent hydrogens do *not* appear in the fumarate product when fumarate itself was the original form of the ligand, but only when fumarate is formed by isomerization from maleate during the reaction. It is believed that different reaction paths exist for the two isomers.[46]

A significant change takes place during the transfer of maleato or fumarato that is esterified at the remote carboxyl. A carbomethoxy group (or aldehyde or carboxamido) can serve, just as can carboxyl, as the remote group in a conjugated ligand, but the alkyl group is removed during the reaction. Furthermore, the alkyl group is found bound in the coordination sphere of the chromium(III) product.[46] [Eq. (18).]

The ester hydrolysis proceeds by alkyl-oxygen fission, that is, by carbonium-ion transfer from carboxyl to chromium. This is quite different from the normal mode of ester hydrolysis, in which acyl-oxygen

46. R. T. M. Fraser and H. Taube, *J. Am. Chem. Soc.*, **83**, 2239, 2242 (1961).

fission is known to predominate. Ester hydrolysis, of course, does not take place when methyl succinato is the transferred group, because the lack of conjugation prevents remote attack from occurring.

It is interesting to note that a cyclopropyl ring does not provide conjugation between two carboxyl groups in the reaction.[46] That is, no attack at the remote carboxyl takes place when cyclopropanedicarboxylic acid is used as the ligand.

One can summarize the chemical changes accompanying the use of maleate as a bridging ligand in the Co^{III}-Cr^{II} oxidation-reduction as follows:

1. Attack by chromium(II) occurs both at the remote carboxyl and at the carboxyl bound to the cobalt.

2. Extensive isomerization to fumarate occurs during the lifetime of the binuclear intermediate.

3. Some exchange of ethylenic hydrogens with solvent occurs *during* the reaction.[47]

4. When the remote carboxyl is esterified, attack may still take place there, but transfer of the alkyl group to chromium occurs.

It is believed that there are two different reaction paths for the maleate and fumarate systems. If we examine the simpler fumarate system, in which no isomerization is expected (or observed) and in which no hydrogen exchange with solvent takes place, the reaction path can be rationalized as in Eq. (19). The oxidation states of the chromium and cobalt are indicated merely by their ionic charges. If the formulas in (19) are written with completely ionic metal-ligand bonds, the reaction corresponds to a transfer of an electron from chromium to fumarate to form a fumarate radical anion. The latter can transfer an electron to cobalt to complete the reduction as it expels a proton from the other carboxyl, as in Eq. (20).

When the remote carboxyl bears a methyl group, the scission of the alkyl-oxygen bond (which is required if the ligand is to be transferred to chromium) can be conveniently effected by displacement by a water molecule in the coordination sphere of the chromium.[48] This nucleophilic displacement on the alkyl carbon will free the bonding electrons

47. The exchange experiments were actually performed with vanadium(II) as the reductant. (Ref. 46.)
48. In the case of the optically active 2-butyl fumarato complex, on the other hand, the alcohol that results from the alkyl-oxygen scission is almost completely racemized (R. T. M. Fraser, *Proc. Chem. Soc.*, **1960**, 317). This is difficult to reconcile with a concerted displacement mechanism.

and allow their distribution down the ligand to the electron-deficient cobalt and carbon atoms [Eq. (21)].

This mechanism does not specify the role of the extra proton that appears in the reaction kinetics. Coplanarity in conjugated systems, however, is always aided by protonation, and coplanarity in the ligand carboxyl is required in this path. In addition, if the proton is located on

$$\tag{19}$$

one of the oxygen atoms to which the cobalt is bonded, the transfer of an electron toward the cobalt will be facilitated as the intermediate complex cleaves.

The maleic-fumaric isomerization path is more difficult to rationalize. Fraser and Taube suggest that an intermediate radical is formed with hydrogen added to the double bond by an electron from the reducing agent and a proton from the solvent.[46]

A particularly interesting example of a chemical change occurring in an organic ligand has been reported by Svatos and Taube.[49] They

49. G. Svatos and H. Taube, *J. Am. Chem. Soc.*, **83**, 4172 (1961).

observed that malonic acid could serve as a bridging group in the Co^{III}-Cr^{II} reaction. Despite the lack of conjugation between the two carboxyls in malonic acid, the form of the reaction kinetics indicated that transfer

$$\text{(20)}$$

of the ligand from cobalt to chromium took place by attack by chromium at the remote carboxy group. Accompanying this transfer was an exchange of the methylene hydrogens with the solvent hydrogens.

$$\text{(21)}$$

The rate law for the oxidation reveals the three possible paths—the acid-independent path, the inverse acid-dependent (anion) path, and the acid-dependent path.

$$\text{Rate} = k_1 + \frac{k_2 \, K_{HA}}{[H^+]} + k_3[H^+]$$

Significantly, the last term, which is diagnostic of remote attack, is missing when diethylmalonic acid is the bridging group, just as it is when succinic acid functions as the bridge. Loss of hydrogen from the methylene group of malonic acid is thus necessary for it it to function as a conjugated ligand and allow attack at the remote carboxyl. These results can be rationalized in terms of an acid-catalyzed enolization of malonate ligand enabling it to form a conjugated bridge between the metal ions [Eq. (22)]. As in the earlier cases, the odd electron transferred into the bridge by the chromium can be located on more than one atom.

The planar, conjugated complex will then decompose to form a product in which the malonato group in its enolized form is attached to chromium [structure (III)]. Ketonization will then occur, the solvent supplying the proton for the central carbon.

(III)

Autoxidation of Metal Chelates

Arnett et al.[50-52] have recently studied the destructive autoxidation of metal chelates, such as iron(III) acetylacetonate [shown in Eq. (23) with only one chelated group in detail] with molecular oxygen. They found that the reaction, which, surprisingly, is not a chain process, only proceeds readily with those metals, chiefly transition metals, that are capable of facile oxidation-reduction. Iron(III) acetylacetonate-$3d$ (the

$$\underset{\quad}{\text{OH}} \quad \underset{\quad}{\text{O}}$$

chelate of $CH_3C{=}CDCCH_3$) was oxidized at the same rate as the protio compound, showing that hydrogen abstraction from this position is not rate-determining.

The reaction bears little similarity to conventional metal-catalyzed chain mechanisms for autoxidation; the oxidation of iron(III) acetylacetonate is not inhibited by conventional antioxidants, and, furthermore, benzoyl peroxide and azobisisobutyronitrile, which are normally initiators of autoxidation, actually inhibit this reaction. The mechanism

$$\begin{matrix} H_3C \\ \quad \searrow \\ HC \quad C-O \\ \quad \searrow \quad \searrow \\ \quad C=O \\ H_3C \end{matrix} Fe\ acac_2 + O_2 \rightarrow Fe^{III} + CH_3C{-}CCH_3 + CO_2 + CH_3CO_2H,\ etc.$$

(23)

acac = acetylacetonate

advanced by Arnett et al. is shown in Eq. (24), although they point out that several others can be devised that fit the kinetic requirements. A homolytic, thermal decomposition of the iron(III) chelate will produce iron(II) and a peroxyradical, I. The latter will undergo ring-opening to produce the open-chain radical, which then reacts with molecular oxygen to give II.

The peroxyradical (II) would be expected to produce 2,3,4-pentanetrione (III) since the decomposition of radicals of structure $R_2CHOO\cdot$ is known to follow the course shown in Eq. (24). The trione is an entirely reasonable intermediate, since it is known[53, 54] to decompose to give the same products as are found in the autoxidation reaction.

50. M. Mendelsohn, E. M. Arnett, and H. Freiser, *J. Phys. Chem.*, **64**, 660 (1960).
51. E. M. Arnett, H. Freiser, and M. A. Mendelsohn, *J. Am. Chem. Soc.*, **84**, 2482 (1962).
52. E. M. Arnett and M. A. Mendelsohn, *J. Am. Chem. Soc.*, **84**, 3821, 3824 (1962).
53. G. A. Russell, *J. Am. Chem. Soc.*, **79**, 3871 (1957).
54. T. G. Traylor and P. D. Bartlett, *Tet. Let.*, **24**, 30 (1960).

The inhibition caused by radical sources can be explained in terms of this mechanism. The thermal decomposition of the chelate produces

$$
\begin{array}{c}
\text{H}_3\text{C} \\
\quad\diagdown \\
\text{HC} \diagdown\kern-1.2em\diagup \text{C—O} \\
\quad\diagup \quad\text{C=O} \\
\text{H}_3\text{C}
\end{array}\text{Fe}^{\text{III}}\ \text{acac}_2 \rightarrow
\begin{array}{c}
\text{H}_3\text{C} \\
\quad\diagdown \\
\text{HC} \diagdown\kern-1.2em\diagup \text{C—O} \\
\quad\diagup \quad\text{C—O} \\
\text{H}_3\text{C} \qquad \cdot
\end{array} + \text{Fe}^{\text{II}}\ \text{acac}_2
$$

(I)

$$
\begin{array}{c}
\text{H}_3\text{C} \\
\quad\diagdown \\
\text{HC} \diagup\kern-1.2em\diagdown \text{C=O} \\
\quad\diagup \quad\text{C=O} \\
\text{H}_3\text{C}
\end{array}
\xrightarrow{\text{O}_2}
\begin{array}{c}
\text{H}_3\text{C} \\
\quad\diagdown \\
\cdot\text{OOHC} \diagup\kern-1.2em\diagdown \text{C=O} \\
\quad\diagup \quad\text{C=O} \\
\text{H}_3\text{C}
\end{array}
\rightarrow \rightarrow
\begin{array}{c}
\text{H}_3\text{C} \\
\quad\diagdown \\
\text{O=C} \diagup\kern-1.2em\diagdown \text{C=O} \\
\quad\diagup \quad\text{C=O} \\
\text{H}_3\text{C}
\end{array}
$$

(II)   (III)

(24)

intermediate radicals of considerable stability that have little interest in normal inhibitors but that will couple with the highly active radicals produced by decomposition of peroxides or azobisnitriles.

chapter seven | Glycol-cleaving Reagents

There are several reagents in common use that are able to cleave 1,2-diols without causing further degradation of the initial products. These are periodic acid, lead tetraacetate, phenyliodoso diacetate, manganic pyrophosphate, and sodium bismuthate. Of these, the first three are the most frequently used for synthetic and analytic purposes, and, although their mechanisms are similar in many ways, there are important differences. The reaction conditions also differ; periodic acid is ordinarily used in aqueous solution, whereas lead tetraacetate and phenyliodoso diacetate are customarily used in acetic acid solution.

PERIODIC ACID

The early work of Malaprade and Fleury showed that this reagent could cleave 1,2-diols to the corresponding aldehydes or ketones [Eq. (1)]. Evidence for the cyclic ester mechanism (I) for this reaction comes from kinetic and spectroscopic work.[1, 2]

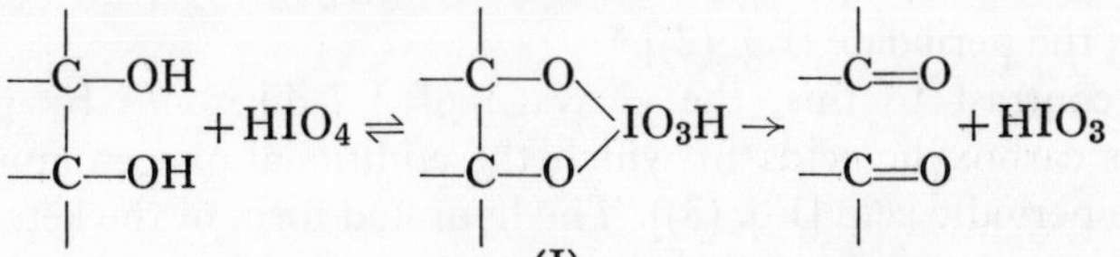

$$
\begin{array}{c}
\mid \\
-\text{C}-\text{OH} \\
\mid \\
-\text{C}-\text{OH} \\
\mid
\end{array}
+ \text{HIO}_4 \rightleftharpoons
\begin{array}{c}
\mid \\
-\text{C}-\text{O} \\
\mid \quad\quad \text{IO}_3\text{H} \\
-\text{C}-\text{O} \\
\mid
\end{array}
\rightarrow
\begin{array}{c}
\mid \\
-\text{C}=\text{O} \\
\\
-\text{C}=\text{O} \\
\mid
\end{array}
+ \text{HIO}_3 \qquad (1)
$$

(I)

1. F. R. Duke, *J. Am. Chem. Soc.*, **69**, 3054 (1947); C. C. Price and M. Knell, *J. Am. Chem. Soc.*, **64**, 552 (1942).
2. G. J. Buist, C. A. Bunton, and J. H. Miles, *J. Chem. Soc.*, **1959**, 743.

Bunton and his colleagues have shown that the reaction is sensitive to steric and conformational effects but is not greatly influenced by electronic effects in the attached groups.[2, 3] That is, ditertiary alcohols, such as pinacol, are cleaved more slowly than disecondary alcohols, such as 2,3-butanediol, because the equilibrium constant for formation of the cyclic ester is smaller, doubtless because of steric compression in the ester. Indeed, the formation of a strained cyclic ester may become the rate-controlling step of the reaction. Those glycols, such as *trans*-9,10-decalindiol and fixed diaxial 1,2-diols, for which cyclic intermediates are impossible, do not react with periodic acid.[4-6]

$$
\begin{array}{cc}
\underset{\displaystyle |}{-\overset{\displaystyle |}{C}-O} \\
\underset{\displaystyle |}{-\overset{\displaystyle |}{C}-O}
\end{array}\!\!\Big\rangle IO_3^- \qquad\qquad
\begin{array}{cc}
\underset{\displaystyle |}{-\overset{\displaystyle |}{C}-O} \\
\underset{\displaystyle |}{-\overset{\displaystyle |}{C}-O}
\end{array}\!\!\Big\rangle IO_4H_2^-
$$

(II)   (III)

The rate variation with pH suggests that the cyclic species that decomposes is the monoanion, structure (II), or its hydrated form, structure (III).

Buist, Bunton, and Miles[2] studied the rates of cleavage of *cis*- and *trans*-1,2-cyclohexanediols and showed that the greater reactivity of the cis than the trans isomer (5-fold for monoanion, pH 4; 160-fold for dianion, pH 9) was caused, not by a greater ease of complex formation, but by a much more rapid breakdown of the complex.

$$
H_5IO_6^* +
\begin{array}{c}
R \\ | \\ R-C-OH \\ | \\ R-C-OH \\ | \\ R
\end{array}
\rightleftharpoons
\begin{array}{c}
R \\ | \\ R-C-O \\ | \\ R-C-O \\ | \\ R
\end{array}\!\!\Big\rangle IO_3^*H \rightarrow 2R_2C{=}O + I^V \qquad (2)
$$

Experiments with oxygen-18 have shown that the oxygens in the carbonyl products, and hence in the cyclic complex, come from the diol, not from the periodate [Eq. (2)].[3]

In contrast to this, the cleavage of 1,2-diketones by periodate produces carboxylic acids in which the additional oxygen atom comes from the periodic acid [Eq. (3)]. The hydrated form of the ketone is not

3. C. A. Bunton and V. J. Shiner, Jr., *J. Chem. Soc.*, **1960**, 1593.
4. J. Honeyman and C. J. G. Shaw, *J. Chem. Soc.*, **1959**, 2451, 2454.
5. S. G. Angyal and R. J. Young, *J. Am. Chem. Soc.,* **81**, 5251, 5467 (1959).
6. V. C. Bulgrin and G. Dahlgren, Jr., *J. Am. Chem. Soc.*, **80**, 3883 (1958).

involved in formation of the cyclic complex;[3, 7] rather the periodate is a nucleophile in this reaction.

$$H_3C-C=O \atop H_3C-C=O \quad + H_3IO_6^= \rightarrow \quad {H_3C-C-O \atop H_3C-C-O}\hspace{-0.3em}\Big\rangle IO_4H_3 \rightarrow 2CH_3CO_2H + I^V \quad (3)$$

The oxidation of the α-hydroxy ketone, methyl acetoin, by periodate is interesting. Bunton and Shiner examined the cleavage of this compound at pH 8, where its rate is at a maximum.[3] They have shown that the oxygen of the acetone is derived from the hydroxyl group of the hydroxy ketone, whereas the additional oxygen in the acetic acid comes from the periodate. It may be that the cyclic intermediate is formed by nucleophilic attack of the periodate oxygen on the carbonyl carbon atom and electrophilic attack of the periodate iodine on the alcoholic oxygen atom. [Eq. (4).]

$$H_3C-C=O \atop {H_3C-C-OH \atop CH_3}} \quad + H_3IO_6^= \rightarrow \quad {H_3C-C-O \atop H_3C-C-O \atop \;\;\;\;\;CH_3}\hspace{-0.3em}\Big\rangle IO_5H_3^= \rightarrow \quad {CH_3CO_2H \atop (CH_3)_2C=O} \quad (4)$$

LEAD TETRAACETATE

This reagent is much less selective than periodic acid, but it does share with the latter the ability to cleave 1,2-glycols to aldehydes or ketones [Eq. (5)]. Criegee, in 1933, suggested that a cyclic intermediate was formed, which then decomposed to products.[8] The decomposition of the cyclic ester has sometimes been written as a heterolytic process and sometimes as a homolytic one; the difficulties in elucidating the bond order and the charge distribution in such a transition state have been referred to earlier (page 20).

In support of the cyclic ester mechanism is the fact that Pb^{IV} can form esters with alcohols, and, most important, that cis glycols are usually cleaved much more rapidly than the trans isomers for which such cyclic forms would be normally less stable. Cis-1,2-cyclopentanediol

7. V. J. Shiner, Jr., and C. R. Wasmuth, *J. Am. Chem. Soc.*, **81**, 37 (1959).
8. R. Criegee, L. Kraft, and B. Rank, *Ann.*, **507**, 159 (1933).

134784

is cleaved 3,000 times faster than the trans isomer; cis-1,2-cyclohexane-diol, 23 times faster than trans. (With large rings, the order may be reversed, and some elegant studies have been made that showed that the relative rates of oxidation of the cis and trans isomers of a series of glycols

$$
\begin{array}{c}
R \\
| \\
R-C-OH \\
| \\
R-C-OH \\
| \\
R
\end{array}
\quad Pb(OAc)_4 \rightleftharpoons \quad
\begin{array}{c}
R \\
| \\
R-C-O-Pb(OAc)_3 \\
| \\
R-C-OH \\
| \\
R
\end{array}
\quad \rightarrow
$$

$$
\begin{array}{c}
R \\
| \\
R-C-O \\
\quad\quad\quad > Pb(OAc)_2 \rightarrow \\
R-C-O \\
| \\
R
\end{array}
\quad
\begin{array}{c}
R \\
| \\
R-C=O \\
\\
R-C=O \\
| \\
R
\end{array}
\quad + Pb(OAc)_2 \quad\quad (5)
$$

could be correlated with the distance between the hydroxyl groups.[5, 8-10] However, with several pairs of cyclohexanediols the trans isomer is cleaved more rapidly than the cis. The cleavage of 9,10-dihydrophenan-threne-9,10-diol illustrates this [Eq. (6)].[11] A similar situation was found

$$
(6)
$$

to obtain with the 9,10-dimethyl derivative of this compound. Only the cis isomer in Eq. (6) reacts with acetone to form a five-membered ketal, structure (IV), analogous to the ester, structure (V), and this suggests that the faster cleavage of the trans isomer is not caused by some un-expected, facile, formation of the trans-ester intermediate. It is true, of course, that the relative stabilities of the cis and trans forms of fused five- and six-ring systems is not always in favor of trans, and, since no

9. V. Prelog, K. Schenker, and W. Kung, *Helv. Chim. Acta*, **36**, 471 (1953).
10. R. J. Dimler, *Advances in Carbohydrate Chem.*, **7**, 37 (1952).
11. E. Boyland and G. Wolf, *Biochem. J.*, **47**, 64 (1940).

intermediates of this type have ever been isolated in lead tetraacetate oxidations, one cannot be certain that the trans isomer is not making use of the cyclic path.

(IV)   (V)

A cyclic-ester intermediate is quite impossible, however, in the case of *trans*-9,10-decalindiol [structure (VI)].[12] Although this compound is cleaved more slowly than the cis isomer, its reaction rate is not abnormally

(VI)

low. It is also cleaved by phenyliodoso diacetate but is not attacked by periodate.[5] This shows clearly that the lead tetraacetate-glycol reaction can proceed by a noncyclic path, but it hardly justifies rejecting the cyclic mechanism completely, as has sometimes been suggested, particularly when one considers the manifold reactions, which lead tetraacetate is able to undergo.

The observation that glycol cleavage is catalyzed by acids[13] and bases[14, 15] and that even isolated primary alcohols[16] can be oxidized by this reagent suggests that the noncyclic mechanisms might be those shown in Eqs. (7) through (9). The noncyclic path appears to be most important for the case of ditertiary diols.

12. R. Criegee, E. Büchner, and W. Walther, *Ber.*, **73**, 571 (1940).
13. R. P. Bell, V. G. Rivlin, and W. A. Waters, *J. Chem. Soc.*, **1958**, 1696.
14. R. Criegee, E. Höger, G. Huber, P. Kruck, F. Marktscheffel, and H. Schellenberger, *Ann.*, **599**, 81 (1956).
15. H. R. Goldschmidt and A. S. Perlin, *Can. J. Chem.*, **38**, 2280 (1960).
16. R. Criegee, *Angew. Chem.*, **70**, 173 (1958).

Primary alcohol oxidation, base-catalyzed:

$$\text{R}-\underset{\underset{\text{H}}{|}}{\overset{\overset{\text{H}}{|}}{\text{C}}}-\text{O}-\text{Pb(OAc)}_3 \rightarrow \text{BH}^+ + \text{R}-\text{C}\underset{\text{H}}{\overset{\text{O}}{\diagup}} + \text{Pb(OAc)}_3^- \qquad (7)$$

$$\text{B}\colon \curvearrowright \quad \text{Pb(OAc)}_3^- \;\rightarrow\; \text{Pb(OAc)}_2 + \text{OAc}^-$$

Glycol oxidation, base-catalyzed:

$$\begin{array}{c} \text{R} \\ | \\ \text{R}-\text{C}-\text{O}-\text{Pb(OAc)}_3 \\ | \\ \text{H}-\text{O}-\text{C}-\text{R} \\ | \\ \text{R} \end{array} \rightarrow \text{BH}^+ + 2\text{R}_2\text{C}{=}\text{O} + \text{Pb(OAc)}_3^- \qquad (8)$$

B:⤴

Glycol oxidation, acid-catalyzed:

$$\begin{array}{c} \text{R} \\ | \\ \text{R}-\text{C}-\text{O}-\text{Pb(OAc)}_3\text{H}^+ \\ | \\ \text{H}-\text{O}-\text{C}-\text{R} \\ | \\ \text{R} \end{array} \rightarrow \begin{array}{c} \text{R} \\ | \\ \text{R}-\text{C}{=}\text{O} \\ \\ \text{HO}{=}\underset{+}{\text{C}}-\text{R} \\ | \\ \text{R} \end{array} + \text{Pb(OAc)}_3\text{H} \rightarrow$$

$$2\text{R}_2\text{C}{=}\text{O} + \text{Pb(OAc)}_2 + \text{HOAc} + \text{H}^+ \qquad (9)$$

In addition to its ability to cleave glycols and to oxidize alcohols to aldehydes, lead tetraacetate can be used to introduce methyl or acetoxyl groups into suitably activated positions in organic compounds.[16] Its reactions with olefins, alkyl ketones, and phenols are illustrated by Eqs. (10) through (12). It undoubtedly operates in the first two cases by

$$\text{C}_6\text{H}_5\text{CH}_3 \xrightarrow{\text{Pb(OAc)}_4} \text{C}_6\text{H}_5\text{CH}_2\text{OAc} \qquad (10)$$

$$(11)$$

$$(12)$$

radical attack,[17] but the third reaction [Eq. (12)] may proceed by heterolytic decomposition of a lead ester as in Eq. (13).

$$\text{(13)}$$

Lead tetraacetate may even add the elements of methyl acetate to double bonds under certain circumstances. Thus, the conversion of styrene to 1-phenylpropyl acetate probably proceeds as follows:

$$Pb(OAc)_4 \rightarrow Pb(OAc)_3 + CH_3CO_2\cdot$$

$$CH_3CO_2\cdot \rightarrow CH_3\cdot + CO_2$$

$$C_6H_5CH{=}CH_2 + CH_3\cdot \rightarrow C_6H_5\overset{\cdot}{C}HCH_2CH_3$$

$$C_6H_5\overset{\cdot}{C}HCH_2CH_3 + Pb(OAc)_4 \rightarrow C_6H_5\overset{\overset{\displaystyle OAc}{|}}{C}HCH_2CH_3 + Pb(OAc)_3$$

$$Pb(OAc)_3 \rightarrow Pb(OAc)_2 + CH_3CO_2\cdot$$

PHENYLIODOSO DIACETATE

This reagent is very similar to lead tetraacetate [Eq. (14)] in that its oxidative ability is not restricted to cleaving vic glycols.[18,19] However, the latter reaction is much slower with phenyliodoso diacetate than with lead tetraacetate. Again a cyclic intermediate is probably involved.

$$\begin{matrix} | \\ -C-OH \\ | \\ -C-OH \\ | \end{matrix} + C_6H_5I(OAc)_2 \rightarrow \begin{matrix} | \\ -C{=}O \\ \\ -C{=}O \\ | \end{matrix} + C_6H_5I + 2HOAc \qquad (14)$$

The reaction of o-nitroaniline with phenyliodoso diacetate yields the products shown in Eq. (15).[20] The azo compound is probably produced by hydrogen-atom abstraction, but it has been suggested that the other

17. D. H. Key, C. J. M. Stirling, and G. H. Williams, *J. Chem. Soc.*, **1954**, 2747, and references therein.
18. R. Criegee and H. Beucker, *Ann.*, **541**, 218 (1939).
19. K. H. Pausacker, *J. Chem. Soc.*, **1953**, 107.
20. L. K. Dyall and K. H. Pausacker, *Australian J. Chem.*, **11**, 491 (1958).

product, an oxadiazole oxide, results from nucleophilic displacement on the trivalent iodine atom of the oxidant by the oxygen of the nitro group, followed by an intermolecular decomposition to products via a seven-

$$NH_2, NO_2 \longrightarrow \begin{cases} NO_2 \quad O_2N \\ \text{-N=N-} \\[4pt] N\text{-}O, \ \overset{+}{N}\text{-}O^- \end{cases} \tag{15}$$

membered ring.[20] However, nitro groups are not noted as particularly effective nucleophiles and nucleophilic attack by the amino group would seem to be a more likely way to initiate the reaction [Eq. (16)]. Heterolysis

$$NH_2, NO_2 + C_6H_5I(OAc)_2 \longrightarrow \overset{+}{N}H_2\bar{I}(C_6H_5)(OAc)_2, NO_2 \xrightarrow[-OAc^-]{-H^+}$$

$$NHI(C_6H_5)OAc, NO_2 \longrightarrow C_6H_5I + OAc^- + HN\text{-}O, \overset{+}{N}\text{=}O \xrightarrow{-H^+} N\text{-}O, \overset{+}{N}\text{-}O^- \tag{16}$$

of the nitrogen-iodine bond in the intermediate in this equation might produce the ion

$$\overset{+}{N}H, NO_2$$

which would immediately cyclize to the heterocycle. It seems more likely, however, that such a discrete entity is never fully formed, but, instead, the rupture of the nitrogen-iodine bond is aided by nitrogen-oxygen bond formation.

MANGANIC PYROPHOSPHATE

Manganic ion, Mn^{3+}, is stable only in very acidic solution ($\sim 9\,N$ H_2SO_4) where it exists as the cherry-red cation. In less acidic solution, it disproportionates to Mn^{2+} and MnO_2. However, Mn^{III} can be complexed with such ions as pyrophosphate to form the ion $Mn(H_2P_2O_7)_3{}^{3-}$,

$$RCH_2C\overset{O}{\underset{H}{\diagdown}} \xrightarrow[\text{slow}]{H^+} RCH{=}\overset{OH}{\underset{}{C}}{-}H \xrightarrow[\text{fast}]{Mn^{III}} RCHC\overset{OH}{\underset{}{}}\overset{O}{\underset{H}{\diagdown}} \qquad (17)$$

stable in neutral solution. Waters[21,22] has conducted some elegant investigations of the oxidation of organic compounds with this reagent. He has shown that it does not attack ordinary alcohols and olefins and that this is probably a result of Mn^{III} being a 1-equivalent oxidant rather than the 2-equivalent reagent these substrates prefer.

$$\begin{array}{l} CH_3 \\ | \\ H_3C{-}C{-}OH \\ | \\ H_3C{-}C{-}OH \\ | \\ CH_3 \end{array} + Mn(H_2P_2O_7)_3{}^{3-} \rightleftharpoons \begin{array}{l} CH_3 \\ | \\ H_3C{-}C{-}O \\ | \\ H_3C{-}C{-}O \\ | \\ CH_3 \end{array}\!\!\!\diagdown Mn^{III} \rightarrow$$

$$\begin{array}{l} CH_3 \\ | \\ H_3C{-}C{=}O \\ \\ H_3C{-}\overset{\cdot}{C}{-}OH \\ | \\ CH_3 \end{array} + Mn^{II} \qquad (18)$$

Manganese(III) oxidizes aldehydes and ketones that are able to enolize, and, significantly, the reactions are zero-order in oxidant but first-order in carbonyl compound and in acid.[23] Presumably, enolization is the rate-controlling step [Eq. (17)]. (Compare with Co^{III}, Ce^{IV}, and V^V oxidations, Chapter 6.) The α-hydroxyaldehydes, which are the first products of this reaction, are, in turn, oxidized further.

21. W. A. Waters, *Quart. Revs. (London)*, **1958**, 277.
22. W. A. Waters, in J. W. Cook and W. Carruthers (eds.), *Progress in Organic Chemistry*, Butterworths, London, 1961.
23. A. Y. Drummond and W. A. Waters, *J. Chem. Soc.*, **1953**, 440.

The oxidation of α-glycols by manganic pyrophosphate has been thoroughly studied. Pinacol is believed to form a cyclic complex by displacing a pyrophosphate group coordinated to Mn^{III}. This can then decompose to give acetone, a manganese(II) complex, and a radical that is rapidly oxidized by a second mole of oxidant.[24] [Eq. (18).] As can be seen, the analogy between this mechanism and that for periodic acid and lead tetraacetate cleavage of glycols is not exact. Furthermore, the relative rates of oxidation of cis and trans isomers differ considerably from those found for those reagents.[25] This is probably because Mn^{III} is a 1-equivalent reagent and the cyclic complex undergoes homolytic scission to generate a molecule of radical. The cyclic compounds of Pb^{IV} and I^{VII}, on the other hand, collapse to give nonradical products.

Induced oxidations by Mn^{III} are indicated by oxygen uptake during many reactions, and this is not surprising in view of the radical intermediates, which are believed formed.

24. A. Y. Drummond and W. A. Waters, *J. Chem. Soc.*, **1953**, 3119.
25. P. Levesley, W. A. Waters, and A. N. Wright, *J. Chem. Soc.*, **1956**, 840.

chapter eight | Nonmetal Oxides and Acids

The oxides of nitrogen, sulfur, and selenium are frequently used oxidants for organic substrates. Sulfur and selenium compounds, whose stable oxidation states differ by two units, are, as would be expected, invariably 2-equivalent reagents. The several stable oxidation states of nitrogen, on the other hand, allow the oxides and acids of nitrogen to function as both 1- and 2-equivalent reagents.

SELENIUM DIOXIDE

Selenium dioxide was introduced by Riley in 1932 as a specific oxidant for the conversion of α-methylene ketones to 1,2-diketones.[1] It was subsequently shown to be able to effect allylic oxidations and certain dehydrogenations.[2]

$$\underset{\substack{\|\\O}}{-CH_2C-} \xrightarrow{\text{SeO}_2} \underset{\substack{\|\;\|\\O\;O}}{-C-C-}$$

$$-CH_2CH{=}CH- \xrightarrow{\text{SeO}_2} -CHOHCH{=}CH-$$

$$\underset{\substack{\|\\O}}{-C-}CH_2CH_2\underset{\substack{\|\\O}}{-C-} \xrightarrow{\text{SeO}_2} \underset{\substack{\|\\O}}{-C-}CH{=}CH\underset{\substack{\|\\O}}{-C-}$$

The reactions are usually run in alcohol or acetic acid solution, but the oxidant itself is prepared in aqueous solution and is, in fact, selenious acid, H_2SeO_3, an acid comparable in strength to acetic acid. The

1. H. L. Riley, J. F. Morley, and N. A. Friend, *J. Chem. Soc.*, **1932**, 1875.
2. N. Rabjohn, in *Organic Reactions*, vol. V, Wiley, New York, 1949, p. 331.

mechanism of the selenium dioxide oxidation of ketones has been studied by Melnikov and Rokitskaya,[3] Duke,[4] and most recently, Corey and Schaefer.[5] The last examined in the greatest detail the conversion of desoxybenzoin to benzil in 70 per cent acetic acid and found that the reaction proceeds by an acid-catalyzed path and a base- (acetate ion) catalyzed path.

$$C_6H_5CH_2\overset{\overset{\displaystyle O}{\|}}{C}C_6H_5 + SeO_2 \rightarrow C_6H_5\overset{\overset{\displaystyle O}{\|}}{C}—\overset{\overset{\displaystyle O}{\|}}{C}C_6H_5 + Se + H_2O$$

$$v = k_1[\text{ketone}]\,[\text{SeO}_2]\,[\text{H}^+] + k_2[\text{ketone}]\,[\text{SeO}_2]\,[\text{OAc}^-]$$

For the acid-catalyzed reaction, the effect of ring substituents was found to be virtually identical with their effect on acid-catalyzed enolization, and the indifference of the rate to the presence of substituents ortho to the carbonyl group suggests that addition to this group is not occurring. There is a deuterium-isotope effect of 6:1 for the oxidation of

$$C_6H_5CD_2\overset{\overset{\displaystyle O}{\|}}{C}C_6H_5$$

by the acid-catalyzed route at 89° and an isotope effect of over 7:1 for the base-catalyzed route at the same temperature. These and other considerations led Corey and Schaefer to suggest for the acid- and base-catalyzed reaction paths the mechanism of Eqs. (1) and (2), which bear an obvious resemblance to enolization processes:

Acid-catalyzed mechanism:

$$C_6H_5\overset{\overset{\displaystyle O}{\|}}{C}CH_2C_6H_5 + H_3SeO_3^+ + H_2O \xrightarrow{\text{slow}}$$

$$C_6H_5\overset{\overset{\displaystyle OSeO_2H}{|}}{C}{=}CHC_6H_5 + H_3O^+ + H_2O$$

$$C_6H_5\overset{\overset{\displaystyle OSeO_2H}{|}}{C}{=}CHC_6H_5 \xrightarrow{\text{fast}} C_6H_5\overset{\overset{\displaystyle O}{\|}}{C}—\overset{\overset{\displaystyle OSeOH}{|}}{C}HC_6H_5 \xrightarrow{\text{fast}}$$

$$C_6H_5\overset{\overset{\displaystyle O}{\|}}{C}—\overset{\overset{\displaystyle O}{\|}}{C}C_6H_5 + Se + H_2O \qquad (1)$$

3. N. N. Melnikov and M. S. Rokitskaya, *J. Gen. Chem. U.S.S.R.*, **7**, 1532 (1937); **15**, 657 (1945); and intervening papers. See *C. A.*, **31**, 8502 (1937); **40**, 5702 (1946).
4. F. R. Duke, *J. Am. Chem. Soc.*, **70**, 419 (1948).
5. E. J. Corey and J. P. Schaefer, *J. Am. Chem. Soc.*, **82**, 918 (1960).

The rate-controlling step in the case of desoxybenzoin is the first step, the formation of the enol selenite ester; but, with strongly electron-withdrawing groups in the "benzyl" ring, the rearrangement to the selenium(II) ester becomes slow enough to affect the rate.

Acetate-catalyzed mechanism:

$$C_6H_5\overset{\overset{O}{\|}}{C}CH_2C_6H_5 + H_2SeO_3 + OAc^- \rightleftharpoons C_6H_5\overset{\overset{OSeO_2^-}{|}}{C}{=}CHC_6H_5 + HOAc + H_2O$$

(2)

The formation of the enol selenite ester is accomplished in this case by means of electrophilic attack by neutral selenious acid on the carbonyl oxygen and removal of the α-proton by acetate ion. Addition of acetate thus facilitates the formation of the selenite ester, but its effectiveness is somewhat diminished by its ability to convert selenious acid partly to the inactive electrophile $HSeO_3^-$. The selenite ester then decomposes to products as shown, although structural changes or addition of bases may shift the rate-controlling step to one that is later in the sequence.

The mechanism of the dehydrogenation of 1,4-diketones by selenium dioxide has also been studied.

$$ArCCH_2CH_2CAr \xrightarrow{SeO_2} ArCCH{=}CHCAr$$

Barton et al.,[6, 7] observed a parallel between the rate of enolization of a series of these ketones and the rate of oxidation. They suggested that the reaction may proceed through the enol. However, enolization itself cannot be rate-controlling, since a subsequent kinetic study showed that a term in selenious acid was present in the kinetics. (This term is a first-order one for both the acid- and the base-catalyzed reactions but is an enigmatic half-order in the absence of catalysis.) The presence of a deuterium-isotope effect in the oxidation shows that enolization cannot be a rapid preequilibrium step.

Banerji, Barton, and Cookson also noted the possibility that the selenium dioxide might remove the pair of hydrogens in a concerted step.[7] A more attractive mechanism, suggested by Schaefer,[8] is similar to that previously elucidated for the conversion of desoxybenzoin to

6. C. S. Barnes and D. H. R. Barton, *J. Chem. Soc.*, **1953**, 1419.
7. J. C. Banerji, D. H. R. Barton, and R. C. Cookson, *J. Chem. Soc.*, **1957**, 5041.
8. J. P. Schaefer, *J. Am. Chem. Soc.*, **84,** 713, 717 (1962).

benzil [Eq. (3)]. The formation of the enol selenite ester probably occurs in a concerted process in the case of acetate-ion catalysis. The decomposition of the enol selenite ester may occur directly by 1,4-elimination,

$$
\begin{array}{c}
\underset{\parallel}{O} \qquad \underset{\parallel}{O} \\
C_6H_5CCH_2CH_2CC_6H_5 + H_2SeO_3 + H^+ \searrow \\
\\
\underset{\parallel}{O} \qquad \underset{\parallel}{O} \\
C_6H_5CCH_2CH_2CC_6H_5 + H_2SeO_3 + OAc^- \nearrow
\end{array}
\qquad
\begin{array}{c}
O-SeO_2H \quad \underset{\parallel}{O} \\
\mid \\
C_6H_5C{=}CH-CHCC_6H_5 \\
\mid \\
H
\end{array}
$$

$$\Big\downarrow \text{fast}$$

$$
\underset{\parallel}{O} \qquad \qquad \underset{\parallel}{O} \\
C_6H_5CCH{=}CHCC_6H_5 + H^+ + SeO_2H^-
$$

$$(3)$$

as indicated, or by rapid rearrangement to a Se^{II} ester (analogous to that postulated for the desoxybenzoin-benzil reaction), which can then lose elements of H_2SeO_2 by a 1,2-elimination. The Se^{II} product could then disproportionate to Se^0 and Se^{IV}.

DIMETHYL SULFOXIDE

It has been found that dimethyl sulfoxide is a useful reagent in the organic laboratory for the oxidation of alkyl tosylates or halides to aldehydes and of epoxides to α-hydroxy ketones. These reactions probably proceed via sulfonium salt intermediates [Eqs. (4)].[9] The decomposition

$$RCH_2OTs + Me_2SO \longrightarrow RCH_2-O-\overset{+}{S}Me_2 + TsO^-$$

$$
\begin{array}{c}
H \\
\mid \\
R-C-O-\overset{+}{S}Me_2 \longrightarrow RCHO + H^+ + Me_2S \\
\mid \\
H
\end{array}
$$

$$
RCH-CHR + Me_2SO \xrightarrow{\ H^+\ }
\begin{array}{c}
OH \quad H \\
\mid \qquad \mid \\
RCH-C-R \\
\mid \\
O-SMe_2 \\
+
\end{array}
\qquad (4)
$$
$$\overset{\diagdown O \diagup}{}$$

$$
\begin{array}{c}
OH \quad H \\
\mid \qquad \mid \\
RCH-C-R \\
\mid \\
O-SMe_2 \\
+
\end{array}
\longrightarrow
\begin{array}{c}
OH \\
\mid \\
RCH-C-R + H^+ + Me_2S \\
\parallel \\
O
\end{array}
$$

9. S. G. Smith and S. Winstein, *Tetrahedron*, **3**, 317 (1958).

of the above sulfonium ions is analogous to the ester mechanism for the chromic acid–alcohol reaction (page 37) in that the oxygen atom loses its attached group together with the bonding electrons.[10]

OXIDES AND ACIDS OF NITROGEN

Both nitric acid and nitrous acid are fairly common oxidants in the organic laboratory. The former bears some resemblance to chromic acid in its oxidation reactions, both being strong acids whose reactivity is negligible in basic solution.[10] Nitrous acid oxidations of ketones often proceed by nitrosations involving the nitrosonium ion NO^+ and the enol form of the ketone. (In basic solution, an alkyl nitrite is usually used; this reacts with the enol anion of the ketone to form the nitrosoketone.) The nitrosoketone, which is in equilibrium with the diketone monoxime, is then hydrolyzed to the α-diketone [Eqs. (5)].

$$H^+ + HNO_2 \rightleftharpoons NO^+ + H_2O$$

$$\underset{\displaystyle RCH_2\overset{\textstyle O}{\overset{\|}{C}}-R}{} \overset{H^+}{\rightleftharpoons} \underset{\displaystyle RCH=\overset{\textstyle OH}{\overset{|}{C}}-R}{}$$

$$\underset{\displaystyle RCH=\overset{\textstyle OH}{\overset{|}{C}}-R}{} + NO^+ \rightarrow \underset{\displaystyle \underset{NO}{\overset{|}{RCH}}-\overset{\textstyle ^+OH}{\overset{\|}{C}}-R}{} \rightarrow \underset{\displaystyle \underset{NO}{\overset{|}{RCH}}-\overset{\textstyle O}{\overset{\|}{C}}-R}{} + H^+ \qquad (5)$$

$$\underset{\displaystyle \underset{NO}{\overset{|}{RCH}}-\overset{\textstyle O}{\overset{\|}{C}}-R}{} + H_2O \overset{H^+}{\rightarrow} \underset{\displaystyle R-\overset{\textstyle O}{\overset{\|}{C}}-\overset{\textstyle O}{\overset{\|}{C}}-R}{} + H_2NOH$$

Dinitrogen tetroxide, N_2O_4, is an excellent reagent for the oxidation of benzyl alcohols to aldehydes,[11] aryl carbinols to aryl ketones,[12] and alkyl sulfides to sulfoxides.[13] There is no doubt that the reactions of this reagent with some substrates, for example, alkenes, proceed via radical intermediates formed by addition of $\cdot NO_2$ to the double bond.[14, 15]

10. L. S. Levitt, *J. Org. Chem.*, **20**, 1297 (1955).
11. B. O. Field and J. Grundy, *J. Chem. Soc.*, **1955**, 1110.
12. J. Grundy, *J. Chem. Soc.*, **1957**, 5087.
13. C. C. Addison and J. C. Sheldon, *J. Chem. Soc.*, **1956**, 2705.
14. H. Schechter, J. J. Gardikes, and A. H. Pagano, *J. Am. Chem. Soc.*, **81**, 5420 (1959).
15. J. C. D. Brand and I. D. R. Stevens, *Chem. & Ind. (London)*, **1956**, 469.

On the other hand, the reaction of N_2O_4 with alcohols is known to produce nitrite esters[16] that undergo clean hydrolysis to regenerate the alcohol [Eq. (6)].[17] The oxidation products probably result from the thermal decomposition of the nitrite esters.[18]

$$RCH_2OH + N_2O_4 \rightarrow HNO_3 + RCH_2ONO \begin{array}{c} \xrightarrow{OH^-} RCH_2OH + NO_2^- \\ \xrightarrow{\Delta} RCHO + NO \end{array} \quad (6)$$

The Nitrous Acid Oxidation of Reductones

Reductone is the name given to a class of readily oxidized natural products characterized by an enediol structure stabilized by conjugation with a carbonyl or similar group. Reductones, such as ascorbic acid, are

$$\text{O=} \overset{HO\ OH}{\underset{O}{\diagdown}} \text{CHOHCH}_2\text{OH} + 2HNO_2 \rightarrow \text{O=} \overset{O\ O}{\underset{O}{\diagdown}} \text{CHOHCH}_2\text{OH} + 2NO + 2H_2O \quad (7)$$

oxidized quantitatively by nitrous acid to dehydroreductones [Eq. (7)]. Bunton, Dahn, and Loewe[19,20] have studied the mechanism of this reaction and have shown that the principal oxidation path in the regions pH 3 to 4 is zero-order in ascorbic acid and second-order in nitrous acid.

$$k \propto [HNO_2]^2$$

In strongly acid solution, the reaction is slower and becomes first-order in each of ascorbic acid, nitrous acid, and the proton.

$$k \propto [HNO_2] [\text{ascorbic acid}] [H^+]$$

The decrease in oxidation rate on acidification is caused by the conversion of the ascorbate anion to the less reactive ascorbic acid (pK = 4.17). The reaction at lower acidity is probably governed by the rate of production of N_2O_3.

$$2HNO_2 \xrightarrow{\text{slow}} N_2O_3 + H_2O$$

$$N_2O_3 + \text{ascorbate ion} \xrightarrow{\text{fast}} \text{products}$$

16. A. D. Yoffe and P. Gray, *J. Chem. Soc.*, **1951**, 1412.
17. M. Anbar, I. Dostrovsky, D. Samuel, and A. D. Yoffe, *J. Chem. Soc.*, **1954**, 3603.
18. P. Gray and A. Williams, *Chem. Revs.*, **59**, 283 (1959).
19. C. A. Bunton, H. Dahn, and L. Lowe, *Nature*, **183**, 163 (1959).
20. H. Dahn, L. Loewe, and C. A. Bunton, *Helv. Chim. Acta*, **43**, 320 (1960).

At higher acidities, the reaction path is the following:

$$HNO_2 + H^+ \rightleftharpoons H_2NO_2^+$$

$$H_2NO_2^+ + \text{ascorbic acid} \xrightarrow{\text{slow}} \text{products}$$

Bunton, Dahn, and Loewe suggest that the intermediate first produced when ascorbic acid or ascorbate ion is attacked is a nitrite ester that undergoes rapid homolytic cleavage to a radical and nitric oxide. The radical is then oxidized by a second mole of nitrous acid [Eq. (8)]. Since

$$\tag{8}$$

these proposed reactions follow the rate-controlling step, they are difficult to corroborate. It is believed, however, that the intermediate radical (I) or the radical anion (II) are the initial products in many ascorbic acid reductions. These facile 1-equivalent oxidations can be

attributed to the great stability of the radicals produced. The radical anion (II), for example, is an analog of a semiquinone, the odd electron and the negative charge residing on each of the three singly bonded oxygen atoms. There are four resonance structures that can be drawn for the radical anion, as compared with only two for the neutral radical.

Nitrobenzene

Alkaline nitrobenzene has long been a favored oxidant for cleaving lignins and lignosulfonic acids to smaller fragments.[21,22] In view of the complexity of the substrate and the high pressure and temperature used for the reaction, it is not surprising that nothing is known of the mechanism. The mechanism of the alkaline nitrobenzene oxidation of alcohols is better understood. The reaction of nitrobenzene with methanolic sodium methoxide produces azoxybenzene (formaldehyde and formate ion are the oxidation products).[23]

$$C_6H_5NO_2 \xrightarrow[\text{CH}_3\text{OH}]{\text{NaOCH}_3} C_6H_5N{=}\overset{\overset{\displaystyle O^-}{|}}{N}{}^+{-}C_6H_5$$

Nitrosobenzene and phenylhydroxylamine are known to react in base to produce azoxybenzene, and it is highly probable that they are intermediates in the reaction. A kinetic study of this reaction by Ogata and Mibae[23] shows that electron-withdrawing groups in the aromatic ring speed the reduction, that the rate law contains a second-order term in methoxide ion, that there is an induction period, and that the reaction is slowed down by the presence of peroxides or molecular oxygen. None of the mechanisms suggested for conversion of nitrobenzene to nitrosobenzene is compatible with the last two observations, and the mechanism of this step remains obscure.

Photolysis of Nitrite Esters

A novel photolytic oxidation of a methyl group has been discovered by Barton.[24] The reaction, which is proving to be of considerable synthetic importance,[25] takes the route shown in Eq. (9). The thermal decomposition of nitrite esters does not follow this course, nor does the photolytic reaction, unless the nitrite and methyl groups are contiguous.[26] The conversion of the C-nitroso compound, in Eq. (9), to the aldehyde involves well-known chemistry; the mechanism advanced by Barton et al. for the photolytic part of the reaction is shown in Eq. (10). The first step, the photolysis, produces a radical pair in a solvent cage. The

21. K. Freudenberg and E. Plankenhorn, *Ber.*, **80**, 155 (1947).
22. W. J. Brickman and C. B. Purves, *J. Am. Chem. Soc.*, **75**, 4336 (1953).
23. Y. Ogata and J. Mibae, *J. Org. Chem.*, **27**, 2048 (1962).
24. D. H. R. Barton, J. M. Beaton, L. E. Geller, and M. M. Pechet, *J. Am. Chem. Soc.*, **82**, 2640 (1960); **83**, 4076 (1961).
25. A. L. Nussbaum, F. E. Carlon, E. P. Oliveto, E. Townley, P. Kabasakalian, and D. H. R. Barton, *Tetrahedron*, **18**, 373 (1962).
26. A. L. Nussbaum and C. H. Robinson, *Tetrahedron*, **17**, 35 (1962).

$$
\begin{array}{c}
\underset{H_2}{\text{ON—O}\quad\text{CH}_3} \xrightarrow{h\nu} \underset{H_2}{\text{OH}\quad\text{CH}_2\text{NO}} \rightleftharpoons
\end{array}
$$

$$
\underset{H_2}{\text{OH}\quad\text{CH}=\text{NOH}} \xrightarrow[\text{H}_2\text{O}]{\text{H}^+} \underset{H_2}{\text{OH}\quad\text{CHO}} \qquad (9)
$$

alkoxyl radical, which will be in an excited state as a result of the energy absorption, abstracts a hydrogen from the nearby methyl group; the radical pair then collapses to the nitroso compound.

$$
\underset{H_2}{\text{ON—O}\quad\text{CH}_3} \xrightarrow[]{h\nu} \overset{\text{·NO}}{\underset{H_2}{\text{O·}\quad\text{CH}_3}} \longrightarrow
$$

$$
\overset{\text{·NO}}{\underset{H_2}{\text{OH}\quad\text{CH}_2\text{·}}} \longrightarrow \underset{H_2}{\text{OH}\quad\text{CH}_2\text{NO}} \qquad (10)
$$

chapter
nine

Peroxy Compounds

The chemistry of peroxy compounds has been covered in detail in several recently published books or review articles.[1-5] The purpose of the present chapter is merely to outline briefly some of the oxidation mechanisms involving these compounds.

The reactions of peroxy compounds, i.e., those molecules containing the —O—O— group, depend to some extent on whether or not hydrogen is one of the attached groups. The hydroperoxides, including hydrogen peroxide, have a wider range of reactions than do the ordinary peroxides.

PEROXIDES

The tendency for dialkyl, diaryl, or mixed peroxides to undergo homolytic decomposition to give radicals has been commented on earlier (Chapter 3). Most oxidations in which these peroxides are involved are, in fact, autoxidations involving molecular oxygen, and the role of the peroxide is merely that of an initiator of the radical chain.

$$(RCO_2)_2 \rightarrow 2RCO_2\cdot$$

initiation

$$ArCHO + RCO_2\cdot \rightarrow Ar\overset{\cdot}{C}O + RCO_2H$$

$$Ar\overset{\cdot}{C}O + O_2 \rightarrow ArCO_3\cdot$$

propagation

$$ArCO_3\cdot + ArCHO \rightarrow ArCO_3H + Ar\overset{\cdot}{C}O$$

1. A. G. Davies, *Organic Peroxides*, Butterworths, London, 1961.
2. Y. K. Syrkin, and I. I. Moiseev, *Uspekhi Khim.*, **29**, 425 (1960).
3. V. Karnojitzki, *Les peroxydes organiques*, Hermann, Paris, 1958.
4. C. Walling, *Free Radicals in Solution*, Wiley, New York, 1957.
5. J. O. Edwards, *Peroxide Reaction Mechanisms*, Interscience, New York, 1962.

Alkyl and aryl peroxides can function as oxidants in their own right under certain circumstances. The oxidation of olefins at allylic positions by peroxides, catalyzed by transition metal ions, has been discussed earlier (page 83).

Dehydrogenations can also be effected with radicals generated by the thermal decomposition of such compounds as t-butyl peroxide [Eqs. (1)]. Phenols[6] and amines[7] also undergo radical coupling under the influence of peroxides.

$$(t\text{-BuO})_2 \rightarrow 2t\text{-BuO}\cdot$$

$$ArCH_2R + t\text{-BuO}\cdot \rightarrow Ar\underset{\cdot}{C}HR + t\text{-BuOH} \qquad (1)$$

$$2Ar\underset{\cdot}{C}HR \rightarrow \quad \begin{matrix} ArCHR \\ | \\ ArCHR \end{matrix}$$

Most tertiary amines react initially with benzoyl peroxide by an oxidation-reduction displacement mechanism [Eq. (2)].[8,9] The amine

$$R_3N + C_6H_5\overset{O}{\overset{\|}{C}}\!\!-\!\!O\!\!-\!\!O\!\!-\!\!\overset{O}{\overset{\|}{C}}\!C_6H_5 \rightarrow R_3\overset{+}{N}\!\!-\!\!O_2CC_6H_5 + C_6H_5CO_2^-$$

$$\Updownarrow$$

$$R_3\overset{+}{N}\cdot + \cdot O_2CC_6H_5 \qquad (2)$$

radical cation decomposes in various ways, depending on its structure. N-Bromosuccinimide[10] and tertiary amines react in an analogous manner.[9]

Peroxydisulfate Oxidations

Despite an extraordinarily high oxidation potential (2.0 volts), the oxidation reactions of peroxydisulfate ion (peroxodisulfate ion, per-sulfate ion) are slow in the absence of traces of catalyst, such as silver or copper ions. A further complication in the study of the mechanism of peroxydisulfate oxidations is the inhibiting effect of oxygen and olefins, such as allyl acetate.

6. C. Walling and R. B. Hodgdon, Jr., *J. Am. Chem. Soc.*, **80**, 228 (1958). See also Ref. 8, Chapter 3.
7. R. L. Huang, *J. Chem. Soc.*, **1959**, 1816.
8. L. Horner and H. Junkermann, *Ann.*, **591**, 53 (1955).
9. H. J. Dauben, Jr., and L. McCoy, *J. Am. Chem. Soc.*, **81**, 4863 (1959).
10. Many of the reactions brought about by N-bromosuccinimide result in a formal oxidation of the substrate. For a review of the reactions of this reagent, see Ref. 9 and R. Filler, *Chem. Revs.*, **63**, 21 (1963).

The uncatalyzed oxidation of i-propyl alcohol by peroxydisulfate has been elucidated by Wiberg.[11] He showed that a chain process was initiated by the first-order decomposition of $S_2O_8^=$ to the sulfate radical anion. The latter is regenerated in a subsequent step.

$$S_2O_8^= \rightarrow 2SO_4^{-\cdot}$$

$$SO_4^{-\cdot} + H_2O \rightarrow HO\cdot + HSO_4^-$$

$$HO\cdot + (CH_3)_2CHOH \rightarrow H_2O + (CH_3)_2\overset{\cdot}{C}{-}OH$$

$$(CH_3)_2\overset{\cdot}{C}{-}OH + S_2O_8^= \rightarrow (CH_3)_2C{=}O + HSO_4^- + SO_4^{-\cdot}$$

$$(CH_3)_2\underset{\cdot}{C}{-}OH + SO_4^{-\cdot} \rightarrow (CH_3)_2C{=}O + HSO_4^-$$

The catalytic effect of copper ion on the reaction has been attributed to the action of copper(III) produced by a chain reaction.[12]

The oxidation of benzoate ions by peroxydisulfate produces phenyl radicals, whose ultimate fate depends on the identity of the other components of the system.

$$ArCO_2^- + SO_4^{-\cdot} \rightarrow ArCO_2\cdot + SO_4^=$$

$$ArCO_2\cdot \rightarrow Ar\cdot + CO_2$$

Hydroxyl radicals are also present in the system, and they can replace $SO_4^{-\cdot}$ in this reaction. The similarity of the above reaction to the Kolbe electrosynthesis (page 128) has been remarked upon.[13,14]

A recent review of peroxydisulfate reactions has appeared.[15]

Carbonyl-Forming Eliminations

The attack of base on an α-hydrogen atom of an alkyl peroxide (or hydroperoxide) results in a 2-equivalent reaction[16] analogous to the

11. K. B. Wiberg, *J. Am. Chem. Soc.*, **81**, 252 (1959). See however L. S. Levitt, B. W. Levitt, and E. R. Malinowski, *J. Org. Chem.*, **27**, 2197 (1962); L. S. Levitt and B. W. Levitt, *Can. J. Chem.*, **41**, 209 (1963).
12. D. L. Ball, M. M. Crutchfield, and J. O. Edwards, *J. Org. Chem.*, **25**, 1599 (1960).
13. F. Fichter and J. Heer, *Helv. Chim. Acta*, **19**, 149 (1936); **18**, 704 (1935).
14. J. Russell and R. H. Thompson, *J. Chem. Soc.*, **1962**, 3379; R. H. Thompson and A. G. Wylie, *Proc. Chem. Soc. (London)*, **1963**, 65.
15. D. A. House, *Chem. Revs.*, **62,** 185 (1962).
16. N. Kornblum and H. E. De La Mare, *J. Am. Chem. Soc.*, **73**, 880 (1951). See also H. E. De La Mare and G. M. Coppinger, *J. Org. Chem.*, **28**, 1068 (1963).

decomposition of nitrate and chromate esters (page 17 and page 38, respectively).

$$B: + H - \overset{|}{\underset{|}{C}} - O - O - Y \rightarrow BH^+ + \,\,{\Large\diagdown}C{=}O + OY^-$$

Naturally, when Y is an acyl group, rather than an alkyl or a hydrogen, the ease of this reaction increases, since the leaving group OY^- has a much greater stability.[17]

HYDROPEROXIDES

Hydroperoxides can also undergo homolytic cleavage to produce radicals, but they are used more frequently in the organic laboratory as 2-equivalent reagents in nonradical, nonchain processes.

The organic peracids are able to oxidize sulfides to sulfoxides; amines to amine oxides, oximes, azo compounds, and nitro compounds; olefins to epoxides; and ketones to esters. The last reaction [Eq. (3)], the Baeyer-Villiger oxidation (page 31), depends on the nucleophilic

$$\overset{O}{\underset{\|}{-C-}} + AOO^- + H^+ \rightleftharpoons \underset{\overset{|}{O-OA}}{\overset{OH}{\underset{|}{-C-}}} \rightarrow \overset{O}{\underset{\|}{-C-O-}} + AOH \qquad (3)$$

$$-NH_2 + AOOH \rightarrow -NHOH + AOH$$

$$-S- + AOOH \rightarrow \overset{O}{\underset{\|}{-S-}} + AOH \qquad (4)$$

$${\Large\diagdown}C{=}C{\Large\diagup} + AOOH \rightarrow {\Large\diagdown}C\overset{O}{\overset{\diagup\diagdown}{\rule{0.9cm}{0.4pt}}}C{\Large\diagup} + AOH$$

character of the peroxy anions for formation of the active intermediate. The others [Eqs. (4)] depend on the electrophilic character of the peroxy oxygen atom. A variety of peracids are used to accomplish these oxidations; Caro's acid, perbenzoic acid, peracetic acid, performic acid, permaleic acid, and perphthalic acid all are readily available, since they exist in equilibrium with a solution of the ordinary acid and hydrogen peroxide.

$$AOH + H_2O_2 \rightleftharpoons AOOH + H_2O$$

17. A. G. Davies, R. V. Foster, and A. M. White, *J. Chem. Soc.*, **1954**, 2200.

The success of the peracids in achieving the oxidations shown above under (4) is due to the ease with which the electrophilic peroxidic oxygen can be transferred to the nucleophile. This, in turn, can be attributed to the fact that acid anions are good leaving groups in nucleophilic substitutions. [Eq. (5).] The transition state for the epoxidation of olefins can be written either as in Eq. (5) (OH$^+$ transfer to the double bond—analogous

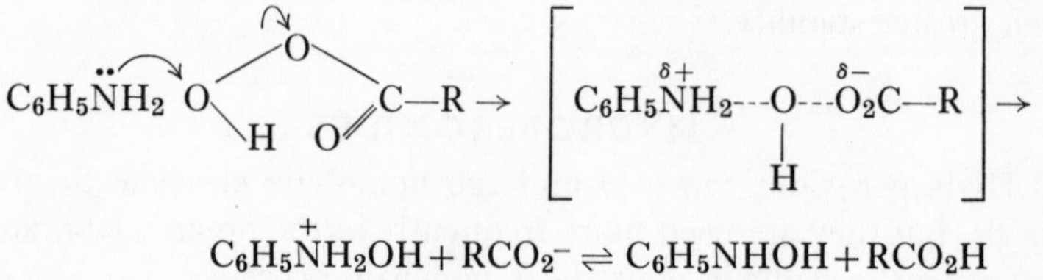

$$C_6H_5\overset{+}{N}H_2OH + RCO_2^- \rightleftharpoons C_6H_5NHOH + RCO_2H \qquad (5)$$

to Br$^+$ transfer in bromine addition) or with the peracid proton being transferred to the carbonyl oxygen [Eq. (6)]. The favorable geometry of this structure and the avoidance of charge production during its formation make it the likely transition state for the epoxidation reaction, particularly in solvents of low polarity. It should be pointed out that a similar, chargeless transition state cannot be written for the amine oxidations.

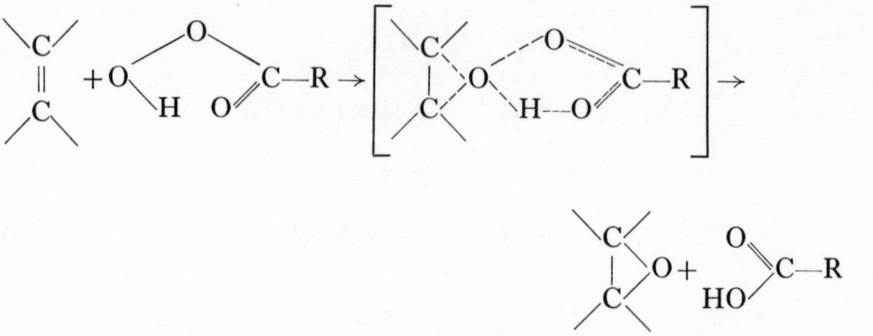

A thorough study of the peracetic acid oxidation of substituted anilines to hydroxylamines and further oxidation products has been made by Ibne-Rasa and Edwards.[18] They find a rho value of -1.86 for this reaction, showing that electron-withdrawing groups drastically slow the rate; polar solvents speed the rate; and radical traps have no effect. These observations strongly support the idea of nucleophilic displacement as the mechanism of the reaction. (The oxidation of anilines by hydrogen peroxide is much slower, since hydroxide ion is a much poorer leaving group in nucleophilic displacements.)

18. K. M. Ibne-Rasa and J. O. Edwards, *J. Am. Chem. Soc.*, **84**, 763 (1962).

Because the entropy of activation is more negative for the reaction in water than for the reaction in ethanol, Ibne-Rasa and Edwards argue that the displacement cannot be a simple one but must involve a molecule of solvent. Thus, for aqueous solution, they write the transition state shown in structure (I). They ascribe the 25-fold rate decrease in going from water to ethanol to the latter's lower acidity rather than to its lower polarity. Entropy changes that accompany solvent polarity changes are often mysterious, however, and a simple nucleophilic displacement may well be the reaction path for this process.

$$CH_3-C\underset{\underset{\displaystyle \overset{\displaystyle O}{H}}{\overset{\displaystyle H \quad\quad H}{O--O}}}{\overset{\displaystyle O}{\diagup}} \overset{\displaystyle Ar}{\underset{}{NH_2}}$$

(I)

Alkyl hydroperoxides, like hydrogen peroxide, are less effective in these reactions than the acyl hydroperoxides (the peracids), probably for these reasons: The alkoxy groups are poorer leaving groups in nucleophilic displacements, and there is no adjacent carbonyl to remove the peroxidic proton intramolecularly.

The peracid oxidation of sulfides to sulfoxides, studied earlier by Overberger and Cummins, also demonstrated the polar character of the peracid oxidations.[19] They used perbenzoic acids with substituents in the ring and found a Hammett rho value of $+1.05$. Electron-withdrawing groups in the peracid ring, thus, speed the reaction by stabilizing the leaving group in agreement with the nucleophilic displacement mechanism.

Reactions of Molecular Oxygen with Nonmetal Ions

The anions of phenols, enols, mercaptans, amines, and methines react with molecular oxygen faster, in general, than do the neutral species. The oxidation products are in some cases dimers and in other cases degradation products. The stability of the anions themselves is a rough measure of their rate of autoxidation, i.e., phenolate ions are, in general,

19. C. G. Overberger and R. W. Cummins, *J. Am. Chem. Soc.*, **75**, 4250 (1953).

much more stable to oxygen than are carbanions. The reactions can be summarized as follows:

$$ZH + OH^- \rightleftharpoons Z^- + H_2O \qquad 1$$

$$Z^- + O_2 \rightarrow ZO_2^- \qquad 2a$$

or

$$2Z^- + O_2 \rightarrow Z—Z + O_2^= \qquad 2b$$

The hydroperoxide anions formed in equilibrium, 2a, may be formed directly by combination of the anions with molecular oxygen[20] or via an intermediate radical chain. The compounds Z—Z are undoubtedly formed by dimerization of the radicals Z· produced as intermediates by reaction of the anions with oxygen.

Whereas neutral phenols and amines undergo autoxidation (although usually at a much slower rate than their anions),[21] many carbon acids are completely inert to oxygen unless they are converted to the anion by base. Thus tris-p-nitrophenylmethane is completely unaffected by molecular oxygen even in the presence of an initiator like azobisbutyronitrile. The anion, however, which is formed in strongly basic solution, rapidly absorbs oxygen to form the hydroperoxide.[22]

$$(p\text{-}NO_2C_6H_4)_3CH + OEt^- \rightleftharpoons (p\text{-}NO_2C_6H_4)_3C^- + EtOH$$

$$(p\text{-}NO_2C_6H_4)_3C^- + O_2 \rightarrow (p\text{-}NO_2C_6H_4)_3COO^-$$

$$(p\text{-}NO_2C_6H_4)_3COO^- + EtOH \rightleftharpoons (p\text{-}NO_2C_6H_4)_3COOH + EtO^-$$

Similarly, Grignard reagents, which have a high degree of carbanion character, absorb oxygen to form hydroperoxides.[23] The anionic forms of ascorbic acid, particularly the dianion, rapidly absorb oxygen.[24] The enolanions of nitroalkanes[25] and ketones[26, 27] also undergo ready autoxidation.

20. H. R. Gersmann and A. F. Bickel, *J. Chem. Soc.*, **1962**, 2356.
21. It is interesting that hindered phenolate ions undergo autoxidation at a greatly accelerated rate. This has been ascribed to the destablizing effect of steric hindrance to solvation of the anion (Ref. 20).
22. M. F. Hawthorn and G. S. Hammond, *J. Am. Chem. Soc.*, **77**, 2549 (1955).
23. C. Walling and S. A. Buckler, *J. Am. Chem. Soc.*, **77**, 6032 (1955).
24. A. Weissberger, J. E. Lu Valle, and D. S. Thomas, Jr., *J. Am. Chem. Soc.*, **65**, 1934 (1943).
25. G. A. Russell, *J. Am. Chem. Soc.*, **76**, 1595 (1954).
26. E. J. Bailey, J. Elks, and D. H. R. Barton, *Proc. Chem. Soc.*, **1960**, 214.
27. W. von E. Doering and R. M. Haines, *J. Am. Chem. Soc.*, **76**, 482 (1954).

The homogeneous oxidation of n-butyl mercaptan by molecular oxygen is also base-catalyzed.

$$n\text{-}C_4H_9SH + CH_3O^- \rightleftharpoons n\text{-}C_4H_9S^- + CH_3OH$$

$$2n\text{-}C_4H_9S^- + O_2 \rightarrow 2C_4H_9S\cdot + O_2^=$$

$$2C_4H_9S\cdot \rightarrow C_4H_9S\text{---}SC_4H_9$$

$$O_2^= + H_2O \rightarrow 2OH^- + \tfrac{1}{2}O_2$$

This reaction has been shown by Wallace and Schriesheim to be strongly solvent-dependent.[28] In solvents, such as dimethyl formamide, containing sodium methoxide as base, the rate of disulfide formation is about 300 times as great as in methanol using the same base. This is undoubtedly related to the increased basicity of the dimethylformamide solutions, since it is known that solvents such as dimethylformamide, dimethyl sulfoxide, pyridine, and tetramethylene sulfone can cause enormous increases in the concentration of the anions of very weak acids and in the rate of base-catalyzed reactions.[29-32] In a similar way, the use of dimethyl sulfoxide-t-butyl alcohol–potassium t-butoxide system greatly accelerates the autoxidation of di- and triphenylmethanes.[33] This is unquestionably due to the increased ionization of these and other carbon acids in this solvent system, since it is the anions that are the active species in the autoxidation.[34]

28. T. J. Wallace and A. Schriesheim, *J. Org. Chem.*, **27**, 1514 (1962).
29. C. H. Langford and R. L. Burwell, Jr., *J. Am. Chem. Soc.*, **82**, 1503 (1960).
30. D. J. Cram, B. Rickborn, C. A. Kingsbury, and P. Haberfield, *J. Am. Chem. Soc.*, **83**, 3678 (1961).
31. R. Stewart and J. P. O'Donnell, *J. Am. Chem. Soc.*, **84**, 493 (1962).
32. R. Stewart, J. P. O'Donnell, D. J. Cram, and B. Rickborn, *Tetrahedron*, **16**, 917 (1962).
33. G. A. Russell, E. G. Janzen, H. Becker, and F. J. Smentowski, *J. Am. Chem. Soc.*, **84**, 2652 (1962).
34. See also H. R. Gersmann, H. J. W. Nieuwenhuis, and A. F. Bickel, *Proc. Chem. Soc.*, **1962**, 279; M. Avramoff and Y. Sprinzak, *Proc. Chem. Soc.*, **1962**, 150; and G. A. Russell, A. J. Moye, and K. Nagpal, *J. Am. Chem. Soc.*, **84**, 4154 (1962).

chapter ten | Some Miscellaneous Oxidants

There are many oxidizing agents that are not conveniently classified either by structure, mechanism, or function. Some of the more interesting oxidation pathways involving several of these reagents are considered in the present chapter. Included are carbonium ions, quinones, anodic oxidations, and the halogens.

CARBONIUM IONS

The empty orbital that carbonium ions possess makes them fairly efficient hydride-ion abstractors; that is, they tend to be 2-equivalent reagents. One exception to this generalization is the reaction of the triphenylmethyl cation with vanadium(II) chloride in acid solution.[1] The product of this reaction is hexaphenylethane, resulting from the dimerization of triphenylmethyl, which, in turn, must have been formed by a 1-equivalent reduction. (A 2-equivalent reduction to the carbanion would immediately produce inert triphenylmethane in the acid medium used.)

$$2(C_6H_5)_3COH \xrightarrow[\text{HCl}]{\text{VCl}_2} (C_6H_5)_3C{-}C(C_6H_5)_3$$

In general, however, the oxidation reactions of carbonium ions are 2-equivalent processes in which hydride ion is abstracted from such reductants as alcohols, ethers, formate ion, or hydrocarbons. Bartlett and McCollum[2] studied the reaction of dianisylmethyl cation and triphenylmethyl cation with several alcohols and ethers, for example,

$$(C_6H_5)_3C^+ + CH_3CH_2OH \rightarrow (C_6H_5)_3CH + CH_3CHO + H^+$$

1. J. B. Conant and A. W. Sloan, *J. Am. Chem. Soc.*, **45**, 2466 (1923).
2. P. D. Bartlett and J. D. McCollum, *J. Am. Chem. Soc.*, **78**, 1441 (1956).

Their systems were complicated by the partial conversion of the alcohols and ethers to their conjugate acids, but their evidence is convincing enough to establish the mechanism of the reaction as a hydride shift from neutral alcohol molecule to cationic carbon. The reactions had activation enthalpies in the region of 14 to 19 kcal mole^{-1} and activation entropies in the range -15 to -26 e.u. The isotope effect for the oxidation of $(CH_3)_2CDOH$ is small, about 2—similar to those found in several other hydride reactions. Moreover, tracer work shows that the hydrogen that becomes attached to the cationic center is clearly that which was attached to the α-carbon of the alcohol; i.e., the transition state is as shown in structure (I).

$$R-\overset{\displaystyle R}{\underset{\displaystyle R}{\overset{\delta+}{C}}}---H---\overset{\displaystyle CH_3}{\underset{\displaystyle CH_3}{C}}=OH^{\delta+}$$

$$(I)$$

Similar results were obtained in a kinetic study of the oxidation of formate ion by the triphenylmethyl cation in formic acid.[3]

$$(C_6H_5)_3C^+ + (H-)CO_2^- \rightarrow (C_6H_5)_3CH + CO_2$$

The activation enthalpy for this step was found to be 18.3 kcal mole^{-1} and the activation entropy -7.5 e.u. The more favorable entropy, compared with the alcohol oxidation of Bartlett and McCollum, is doubtless a reflection of the partial neutralization of charge that accompanies the formation of the transition state in this case.

The more stable the carbonium ion, the less effective oxidant it is; thus, the tri-p-anisylmethyl cation abstracts hydride from isopropyl alcohol only one-thousandth as fast as does the triphenylmethyl cation. The reactivities of the reductant also vary with structure, esters being inferior to alcohols as hydride donors.[4]

Protonation of the reductant—the alcohol, ether, or ester—will naturally reduce its hydride-donor properties; acid, however, is usually required to generate the oxidant, the carbonium ion. Deno et al. have shown that the use of polyphosphoric acid instead of sulfuric acid can help resolve this dilemma. Polyphosphoric acid is a rather ineffective proton donor $(-H_0$ is small) but a fairly effective carbonium-ion generator $[-H_R(J_0)$ is large].[4]

3. R. Stewart, *Can. J. Chem.*, **35**, 766 (1957).
4. N. C. Deno, G. S. Saines, and M. Spangler, *J. Am. Chem. Soc.*, **84**, 3295 (1962).

Hydrocarbons as reductants are not subject to protonation, and strongly acidic conditions can be used to effect their oxidation with carbonium ions. The acid-catalyzed isomerizations of hydrocarbons and the acid-catalyzed alkylation of olefins with isoparaffins have received a great deal of attention in the past 30 years from Ipatieff,[5] Bartlett et al.,[6] Beeck et al.,[7] and, most recently, Hofmann and Schriesheim.[8] There is no doubt that hydride abstraction by carbonium ions occurs in these reactions.

The fairly specific hydride-abstracting properties of carbonium salts[9-11] has been used to advantage in the syntheses of such unusual cationic species as heptalenium ion [Eq. (1)].[11]

$$(C_6H_5)_3C^+BF_4^- + \quad \rightarrow (C_6H_5)_3CH + \quad BF_4^- \quad (1)$$

QUINONES

The ready reversibility of the quinone-hydroquinone couple led to its early use as a means of measuring hydrogen-ion concentration, since the potential of the system varies with the pH of the solution [Eq. (2)].

The electrode potential of a substituted quinone depends on the electronic characteristics of the substituent in the expected way. i.e.,

$$\text{(quinone)} + 2H^+ + 2\epsilon \rightleftharpoons \text{(hydroquinone)} \quad (2)$$

electron-withdrawing groups, such as chloro, raise the potential, shifting the above equilibrium to the right; whereas electron-donating groups, such as methyl, have the opposite effect. In basic solution, resonance-

5. V. N. Ipatieff, *Catalytic Reaction of High Pressures and Temperatures*, Macmillan, New York, 1936, pp. 673ff.
6. P. D. Bartlett, F. E. Condon, and A. Schneider, *J. Am. Chem. Soc.*, **66**, 1531 (1944).
7. D. P. Stevenson, C. D. Wagner, O. Beeck, and J. W. Otvos, *J. Am. Chem. Soc.*, **74**, 3269 (1952).
8. J. E. Hofmann and A. Schriesheim, *J. Am. Chem. Soc.*, **84**. 953, 957 (1962).
9. H. J. Dauben, Jr., F. A. Gadecki, K. M. Harmon, and D. L. Pearson, *J. Am. Chem. Soc.*, **79**, 4557 (1957).
10. H. J. Dauben, Jr., and L. R. Honnen, *J. Am. Chem. Soc.*, **80**, 5570 (1958).
11. H. J. Dauben, Jr., and D. J. Bertelli, *J. Am. Chem. Soc.*, **83**, 4657 (1961).

stabilized semiquinone ions are stable enough to exist in equilibrium with the fully oxidized and reduced forms [Eq. (3)].

$$\tag{3}$$

Quinones with electron-withdrawing substituents, such as chloranil (tetrachloro-1,4-benzoquinone), are useful oxidants in the organic laboratory. These reactions are usually not rapidly reversible, i.e., mechanistic factors are important as well as the potential of the quinone-hydroquinone couple.[12]

$$\tag{4}$$

The mechanism of the dehydrogenation of aromatic compounds by tetrachloro-1,2-benzoquinone has been studied by Jackman and Thompson.[13] They found that the rate of the reaction in Eq. (4) could be correlated with the modified Hammett substituent constant, σ^+, of the group Z, assuming an initial reaction at the 2-position of the dihydro-

$$\tag{5}$$

naphthalene. A charge-transfer complex is formed between the two reactants, and it is reasonable (though not necessary) to assume that this precedes the rate-controlling hydrogen transfer. The correlation with σ^+ and the sign and magnitude of the rho value (-2.5) suggests that the rate-controlling step is a hydride transfer from the 2-position of the dihydronaphthalene to the quinone [Eq. (5)]. (The over-all rho value includes, of course, the rho for complex formation if this precedes the

12. For example, o-quinones are more reactive in dehydrogenations than p-quinones on the basis of their relative redox potentials (E. A. Braude, L. M. Jackman, and R. P. Linstead, *J. Chem. Soc.*, **1954**, 3548).
13. L. M. Jackman and D. T. Thompson, *J. Chem. Soc.*, **1961**, 4794.

rate-controlling step. The rho for complex formation is certain to be negative also, but it would only contribute greatly to the over-all rho if the extent of complex formation at equilibrium was small.) This is followed by a rapid proton transfer to give the naphthalene. It was observed that electron-donating substituents at the 6-position gave somewhat accelerated rates, and this was shown to be due to the shift of the reactive site from C_2 to C_1 in the dihydronaphthalene. Thus, the methoxy group in 6-methoxy-1,2-dihydronaphthalene activates the 1-position to which it is conjugated (corresponding to a para substituent) but not the 2-position (corresponding to a meta substituent) [Eq. (6)].

$$\text{(6)}$$

A comprehensive study of quinones as dehydrogenation agents has been made by Braude, Linstead, Jackman, et al.[14, 15]

ANODIC OXIDATIONS

Heterogeneous oxidation systems have not been considered in this book, and it does not seem appropriate to attempt to treat the very large field of electrode processes here. Nevertheless, it is worth commenting briefly on the anodic oxidation of a few organic molecules and ions.

The electrolysis of carboxylic acid salts, the well-known Kolbe electrosynthesis,[16] produces hydrocarbons in good yield. It was suggested by Brown and Walker in 1891 that the mechanism of this reaction was the direct oxidation of the carboxylate anion at the anode, followed by the decomposition of the radicals so produced.[17] This sequence can be written as follows:

$$RCO_2^- \xrightarrow{-e} RCO_2 \cdot \rightarrow R \cdot + CO_2$$

$$2R \cdot \rightarrow R\text{---}R$$

(The decomposition of the radical intermediates may occur by disproportionation as well as by coupling, i.e., propionic acid produces ethylene as well as butane under certain conditions.[18, 19])

14. Ref. 13, the Ref. listed in Note 12, and intervening papers.
15. See also D. T. Longone and G. L. Smith, *Tetrahedron Letters*, 5, 205 (1962).
16. H. Kolbe, *Ann.*, **69**, 257 (1849).
17. A. C. Brown and J. Walker, *Ann.*, **261**, 107 (1891).
18. P. Holemann and K. Clusius, *Ber.*, **70**, 819 (1937).
19. C. L. Wilson and W. T. Lippincott, *J. Am. Chem. Soc.*, **78**, 4290 (1956).

Several other mechanisms have been advanced in the past 50 years for the Kolbe electrosynthesis,[20] but the work of Wilson and Lippincott has shown that the discharged-ion theory of Brown and Walker is the most satisfactory.[21]

If higher voltages are used (50 to 175 volts), the electrolysis products are more consistent with cation than with radical formation.[22, 23] It seems reasonable to suppose that the initially produced radicals would suffer further electron loss to an electrode at high potential to give a cation rather than to decompose in the usual way.

$$RCO_2^- \xrightarrow{-e} RCO_2\cdot \xrightarrow{-e} R^+ + CO_2$$

The anodic oxidation of aniline in aqueous sulfuric acid follows a different course from that of its N-methyl and N,N-dimethyl derivatives. Adams et al.[24] have shown that aniline is coupled together in a head-to-tail manner to give initially the dimer p-aminodiphenylamine and eventually an octamer called emeraldine.

The dimer is believed to be formed by the coupling of two aniline radical cations formed, in turn, by 1-equivalent reactions. (These could be either one-electron transfers from neutral aniline or hydrogen-atom transfers from the anilinium ion.)

Further coupling can occur in a similar way.

20. S. Glasstone and A. Hickling, *Electrolytic Oxidation and Reduction*, Chapman and Hall, London, 1935, p. 312.
21. See also B. C. L. Weedon, *Quart. Revs. (London)*, **6**, 380 (1952); B. E. Conway and M. Dzieciuch, *Can. J. Chem.*, **41**, 21, 38, 55 (1963).
22. E. J. Corey, N. L. Bauld, R. T. La Londe, J. Casanova, Jr., and E. T. Kaiser, *J. Am. Chem. Soc.*, **82**, 2645 (1960); E. J. Corey and J. Casanova, Jr., *J. Am. Chem. Soc.*, **85**, 165 (1963).
23. B. Wladislaw, *Chem. & Ind. (London)*, **1962**, 1868.
24. D. M. Mohilner, R. N. Adams, and W. J. Argersinger, Jr., *J. Am. Chem. Soc.*, **84**, 3618 (1962).

N,N-Dimethylaniline, on the other hand, gives tetramethyl-benzidine[25] under these conditions, and these products must result from a tail-to-tail coupling either directly or via a benzidine rearrangement. Furthermore, Adams et al.[25] conclude from electrochemical

$$2H^+ + Me_2N-\underset{(I)}{\underbrace{}}-NMe_2 \xrightarrow{-2\epsilon} Me_2\overset{+}{N}=\underset{(II)}{\underbrace{}}=\overset{+}{N}Me_2 \quad (7)$$

evidence that the initial oxidation of N,N-dimethylaniline is a 2-equivalent reaction, probably removal of an electron pair from the neutral amine to give a dication,[26] which then reacts rapidly with a second molecule of amine [Eq. (7)]. Tetramethylbenzidine (I) is formed in the reaction but is then oxidized further to the quinoid form (II) under the electrolysis conditions.

$$Me_2N-\underbrace{}-NMe_2 + C_6H_5CO_2H \quad (8)$$

The benzidines can be produced by chemical oxidation of N-alkyl-anilines also.[27] Presumably, similar reactive intermediates are generated by chemical and electrochemical means.

25. T. Mizoguchi and R. N. Adams, *J. Am. Chem. Soc.*, **84**, 2058 (1962).

26. Hydride removal from $C_6H_5\overset{+}{N}HMe_2$ would yield the same dication. Hydrogen atom, hydride ion, and electron transfers have all been suggested as mechanisms for electrochemical redox reactions. See F. D. Popp and H. P. Schultz, *Chem. Revs.*, **62**, 19 (1962).

27. V. Hanousek and M. Matrka, *Collection Czechoslov. Chem. Commun.*, **24**, 16 (1959).

Curious rearrangements accompany the oxidation of cations like crystal violet and malachite green, (III) in Eq. (8), by chromic acid, lead dioxide, or anodic oxidation. The fact that chemical and anodic oxidations[27, 28] give the same products again suggests that both kinds of

(IV)

oxidations produce the same intermediate. In this case, the coupling of the oxidized dimethylaniline units occurs intramolecularly, probably via an intermediate like structure (IV)[27] that then decomposes to products.

HALOGENS

Alcohols, aldehydes, and hemiacetals are oxidized by bromine in aqueous solution by what appear to be very similar mechanisms. The kinetic studies of Bugarszky, Kaplan, Perlmutter-Hayman, and others show that the reaction is indeed an oxidation, not a bromination, and that bromine is the oxidant, not hypobromous acid; the latter's oxidations are decidedly slower.[29-34] Furthermore, the reaction does *not* involve formation of a hypobromite ester, RCH_2OBr. [The hypobromite ester might be expected to decompose in a manner analogous to that suggested for chromate ester (Chapter 4).]

The deuterium-isotope effect that has been found for the oxidation of CH_3CD_2OH ($k_H/k_D \approx 4$ in acid at 25°) shows that the rate-controlling step requires scission of the C—H bond.[32] The variation of oxidation

28. Z. Galus and R. N. Adams, *J. Am. Chem. Soc.*, **84**, 3207 (1962); *J. Phys. Chem.*, **67**, 862 (1963).
29. S. Bugarszky, *Z. physik. Chem.*, **48**, 63 (1904).
30. L. Farkas, B. Perlmutter, and O. Schächter, *J. Am. Chem. Soc.*, **71**, 2829 (1949).
31. B. Perlmutter-Hayman and A. Persky, *J. Am. Chem. Soc.*, **82**, 276, 3809 (1960).
32. L. Kaplan, *J. Am. Chem. Soc.*, **80**, 2639 (1958).
33. B. Perlmutter-Hayman and Y. Weissman, *J. Am. Chem. Soc.*, **82**, 2323 (1962); see also P. T. McTigue and J. M. Sime, *J. Chem. Soc.*, **1963**, 1303.
34. H. S. Isbell and W. Pigman, *J. Res. Natl. Bur. Standards*, **10**, 337 (1933); **18**, 141 (1937).

rate with pH is particularly illuminating. It shows that the anions of alcohols, aldehydes, and the cyclic hemiacetal D-glucose are oxidized very much faster than are the neutral molecules.

In acid solution (pH 1 to 4), the rates of oxidation of both ethanol and acetaldehyde are about constant, the aldehyde being oxidized several hundred times as fast as the alcohol. As the pH is increased beyond 5, the rate of oxidation of both substrates rises, and it can be shown that the rate becomes proportional to the anion concentration. If an estimate is made of the (very small) degree of ionization of aldehydes and alcohols in neutral solution, one concludes that the anions are oxidized about 10^{10} times as fast as the neutral molecules.[33]

The removal of a hydride ion from the anions by molecular bromine appears to be the most satisfactory mechanism for this reaction.[30, 32, 35]

$$CH_3CH_2OH + OH^- \rightleftharpoons H_2O + CH_3CH_2O^-$$

$$CH_3CH_2O^- + Br_2 \rightarrow CH_3CHO + HBr + Br^-$$

Aldehyde hydrates and their close analogs, hemiacetals, presumably react similarly via the ions [structures (V) and (VI)].

$$\begin{array}{ccc} & \overset{O^-}{\underset{|}{}} & & & \overset{O^-}{\underset{|}{}} \\ R\!-\!\overset{|}{\underset{|}{C}}\!-\!OH & & \text{and} & & R\!-\!\overset{|}{\underset{|}{C}}\!-\!OR \\ & H & & & H \\ & (V) & & & (VI) \end{array}$$

The action of bromine and permanganate on alcohols and aldehyde hydrates are, thus, very similar. Both involve the organic anion, and the facile oxidations are due principally to low energies of activation in each case. It is interesting to note the effect of the oxidant's charge on the activation entropies. The permanganate oxidations have large negative entropies of activation, whereas the bromine oxidations appear to have entropies of activation near 0. The negative charge on both reactants in the permanganate-organic anion reactions is clearly reflected in the unfavorable entropy term.

Hydrocarbons react with bromine by the well-known mechanism of hydrogen-atom abstraction. The abstractor is probably a bromine atom, not a bromine molecule, in all cases, however. Fluorine appears to

35. C. G. Swain, R. A. Wiles, and R. F. W. Bader, *J. Am. Chem. Soc.*, **83** 1945 (1961).

be the only halogen molecule that can directly abstract a hydrogen atom from hydrocarbons.[36]

$$—\overset{|}{\underset{|}{C}}—H + F_2 \rightarrow —\overset{|}{\underset{|}{C}}\cdot + HF + F\cdot$$

Formic acid is oxidized readily to carbon dioxide by chlorine in aqueous solution. The path involving formate ion is some 10^4 times faster than that involving neutral formic acid.[37, 38] This is similar to the discrimination exercised by permanganate. Since a 1-equivalent reaction between chlorine and formate ion is unlikely, a hydride transfer appears to be the most satisfactory mechanism in this case.

$$HCO_2^- + Cl_2 \rightarrow CO_2 + HCl + Cl^-$$

In basic solution, chlorine forms hypochlorite ion, which appears to be unable to oxidize formate ion at all; the effect of the reactants' like charges is clearly seen. In neutral solution, the presence of a second-order term in hypochlorite in the rate law suggests that Cl_2O, which is known to be in equilibrium with hypochlorous acid, is the active oxidant.[39]

Iodine is a weaker oxidant than the other halogens, and, in neutral solution, it does not react with aliphatic aldehydes. In base, the oxidation proceeds rapidly, but it must compete with iodination, which is followed by hydrolytic cleavage.[40, 41] The rate-controlling step of the iodination process is base-catalyzed enolization. [Eq. (9).]

$$CH_3CHO \xrightarrow[OH^-]{I_2} CH_3CO_2^- + CHI_2CHO + CI_3CHO$$
$$\qquad\qquad\qquad\qquad \downarrow OH^- \qquad \downarrow OH^-$$
$$\qquad\qquad\qquad CH_2I_2 + HCO_2^- \quad CHI_3 + HCO_2^- \qquad (9)$$

36. W. T. Miller, Jr., and A. L. Dittman, *J. Am. Chem. Soc.*, **78**, 2793 (1956).
37. E. A. Shilov and A. I. Slyadnev, *Zhur. Fiz. Khim.*, **22**, 1312 (1948); *C. A.*, **43**, 2495 (1949).
38. J. Thamsen, *Acta Chem. Scand.*, **7**, 682 (1953).
39. E. A. Shilov, A. I. Slyadnev, and G. V. Kupinskaya, *J. Gen. Chem. U.S.S.R.*, **22**, 1497 (1952).
40. S. Bose, *J. Indian Chem. Soc.*, **34**, 739, 825 (1957).
41. C. F. Cullis and P. A. Swain, *J. Chem. Soc.*, **1962**, 3348; *ibid.*, **1963**, 1139.

chapter eleven | Biochemical Oxidation Mechanisms

The energy made available by the reaction of molecular oxygen with organic compounds is the ultimate source of power for the vast majority of living systems. Water and carbon dioxide have large negative free energies of formation and the complete oxidation of organic molecules, particularly hydrocarbons and closely related compounds, releases large amounts of energy. The ubiquity of organic compounds and molecular oxygen means that an abundant energy source is always available to living systems. More interesting than gross energy considerations is the marvelously intricate set of chemical mechanisms that controls the rate of energy release and stores much of it as readily available chemical potential energy rather than allowing it to be dissipated as heat. The chemical potential energy is then released by a hydrolytic rather than an oxidative process, although energies of hydrolysis for organic compounds are in general much less than energies of oxidation. In the following chapter are described some of the mechanisms involved in the complex set of processes that result in the ultimate conversion of oxygen and complex organic molecules to carbon dioxide and water.

PYRIDINE NUCLEOTIDE COENZYMES

There are two important pyridinium coenzymes that are found in all living systems and that act as oxidants in many biological processes. They are diphosphopyridine nucleotide (DPN^+) and triphosphopyridine nucleotide (TPN^+). Each is composed of two D-ribose units, an adenylic acid moiety, a pyrophosphate link, and, most important, a carboxamido-pyridinium group. The structure of DPN^+ is shown in (I); TPN^+ is identical except for the presence of an extra phosphate group on one of the ribose units.

DPN+

(I)

That portion of the coenzyme that is reduced during a biological oxidation is the pyridinium ring,[1] and studies with model compounds have produced much useful information about the reaction mechanism.[2,3] Various models have been used, both compounds with structural modifications in the pyridine ring of DPN^+ and TPN^+ and simple compounds, such as N^1-methyl and N^1-benzyl nicotinamide cations.

The reduction of the nicotinamide cation portion of DPN^+ and TPN^+ by a substrate, such as ethanol, in the presence of an enzyme, such as yeast alcohol dehydrogenase, produces a mole of acetaldehyde and the reduced form of the coenzyme (usually written DPNH). Traces of radicals have been detected during the course of the reaction by the ultrasensitive electron-spin resonance technique,[4] but they are probably caused by the presence of adventitious impurities, and more recent studies have failed to detect radical intermediates in the reaction.[5] It is known that direct hydrogen transfer occurs,[6] and it is generally believed

1. P. Karrer and O. Warburg, *Biochem. Z.*, **285**, 297 (1936).
2. F. H. Westheimer, in P. D. Boyer, H. Lardy, and K. Myrback (eds.), *The Enzymes*, vol. 1, Academic, New York, 1959, p. 259.
3. N. O. Kaplan, in P. D. Boyer, H. Lardy and K. Myrback (eds.), *The Enzymes*, vol. 3, Academic, New York, 1960, p. 105.
4. B. Commoner, J. J. Heise, B. B. Lippincott, R. E. Norberg, J. V. Passonneau, and J. Townsend, *Science*, **126**, 57 (1957).
5. H. R. Mahler and L. Brand, in M. S. Blois, Jr., H. W. Brown, R. M. Lemmon, R. O. Lindblom, and M. Weissbluth (eds.), *Free Radicals in Biological Systems*, Academic, New York, 1961, p. 157.
6. F. H. Westheimer, H. F. Fisher, E. E. Conn, and B. Vennesland, *J. Am. Chem. Soc.*, **73**, 2403 (1951).

that the conversion of DPN⁺ to DPNH is a 2-equivalent reaction,[7] probably a hydride transfer from the substrate to the 4-position of the pyridine ring [Eq. (1)].

$$H_2N-\overset{\overset{O}{\parallel}}{C}\underset{\underset{R}{\overset{+}{N}}}{\bigcirc} + SH_2 \rightarrow H_2N-\overset{\overset{O}{\parallel}}{C}\underset{\underset{R}{N}}{\overset{H}{\underset{}{\bigcirc}}} + S + H^+ \tag{1}$$

The structure of the rest of the coenzyme molecule is, as might be expected, highly specific. The deoxyribose analog of DPN⁺, for example, has only slight activity. Further, only one of the possible configurations at the glycosidic linkage between the nicotinamide and the riboside is possible if enzymic oxidation is to occur. A further, more subtle difference exists between the reduction of DPN⁺ and that of a simple model, such as the N¹-methylnicotinamide cation. Oxidation of deuterated ethanol, CH_3CD_2OH, by DPN⁺ results in the transfer of deuterium to the DPN⁺ in a stereospecific manner, some enzymes causing addition of the deuterium to one side of the pyridine ring and others to the opposite side.[8] This is, in fact, an asymmetric synthesis, the mode of complexing between enzyme, coenzyme, and substrate determining the stereochemistry of the reduction. Karrer, Westheimer, and others have used the reduced form of DPN⁺ or TPN⁺ models to effect several chemical reductions.[2] Thus, quinones, malachite green, and thiobenzophenone are each reduced by N-alkyldihydropyridines. Activated double bonds are also able to dehydrogenate certain DPNH model compounds, such as those shown in Eqs. (2) and (3).[9, 10] The attachment of the deuterium to the β-carbon of the fluoro ketone in Eq. (3) is again consistent with a hydride transfer from the dihydropyridine derivative to the substrate to form the enol

7. A 1-electron reduction of an N-alkylpyridinium ion has been reported, however. See W. M. Schwarz, E. M. Kosower, and I. Shain, *J. Am. Chem. Soc.*, **83**, 3164 (1961).
8. H. F. Fisher, E. E. Conn, B. Vennesland, and F. H. Westheimer, *J. Biol. Chem.*, **202**, 687 (1953); A. San Pietro, N. O. Kaplan, and S. P. Colowick, *J. Biol. Chem.*, **212**, 941 (1955); P. Talalay, F. A. Loewus, and B. Vennesland, *J. Biol. Chem.*, **212**, 801 (1955); B. Vennesland, *Discussions Faraday Soc.*, **1955**, 240; J. W. Cornforth, G. Ryback, G. Popják, C. Donninger, and G. Schroepfer, Jr., *Biochem. Biophys. Res. Comm.*, **9**, 371 (1962).
9. E. A. Braude, J. Hannah, and R. P. Linstead, *J. Chem. Soc.*, **1960**, 3249.
10. B. E. Norcross, P. E. Klinedinst, Jr., and F. H. Westheimer, *J. Am. Chem. Soc.*, **84**, 797 (1962).

$$\underset{\underset{\text{CHCO}_2\text{H}}{\overset{\text{CHCO}_2\text{H}}{\|}}}{}\ +\ \underset{\text{Me}}{\overset{\text{EtO}_2\text{C}}{\underset{\overset{|}{\text{N}}}{\underset{\text{H}}{}}}}\underset{\overset{\text{H}\diagup\text{H}}{}}{\diagup}\overset{\text{CO}_2\text{Et}}{\underset{\text{Me}}{}}\ \rightarrow\ \underset{\overset{|}{\text{CH}_2\text{CO}_2\text{H}}}{\text{CH}_2\text{CO}_2\text{H}}\ +\ \underset{\text{Me}}{\overset{\text{EtO}_2\text{C}}{\underset{\text{N}}{}}}\overset{\text{CO}_2\text{Et}}{\underset{\text{Me}}{}} \tag{2}$$

$$\text{H}^+ + \text{C}_6\text{H}_5 - \overset{\overset{\text{O}}{\|}}{\text{C}} - \text{CH}{=}\text{CHCF}_3 + \underset{\text{Me}}{\overset{\text{EtO}_2\text{C}}{\underset{\overset{|}{\text{N}}}{\underset{\text{Me}}{}}}}\overset{\text{D}\diagdown\text{D}}{\diagup}\overset{\text{CO}_2\text{Et}}{\underset{\text{Me}}{}} \rightarrow$$

$$\text{C}_6\text{H}_5 - \overset{\overset{\text{O}}{\|}}{\text{C}} - \text{CH}_2\text{CHDCF}_3 + \underset{\text{Me}}{\overset{\text{EtO}_2\text{C}}{\underset{\overset{+}{\underset{|}{\text{N}}}}{\underset{\text{Me}}{}}}}\overset{\text{D}}{\diagup}\overset{\text{CO}_2\text{Et}}{\underset{\text{Me}}{}} \tag{3}$$

anion. The last will be formed readily because of the polar effect of the trifluoromethyl group as well as the conjugative effect of the carbonyl group.

$$\left[\ \text{C}_6\text{H}_5 - \overset{\overset{\text{O}}{\|}}{\text{C}} - \overset{-}{\text{C}}\text{HCHDCF}_3 \leftrightarrow \text{C}_6\text{H}_5 - \overset{\overset{\text{O}^-}{\|}}{\text{C}}{=}\text{CHCHDCF}_3\ \right]$$

Interestingly enough, the fluoro ketone is not reduced by any of the compounds shown in structures (II) through (IV).[10]

$$\underset{(\text{II})}{\overset{\overset{\text{O}}{\|}}{\text{H}_2\text{N}-\text{C}}\underset{\overset{|}{\text{N}}}{}\underset{\text{CH}_2\text{C}_6\text{H}_5}{}} \qquad \underset{(\text{III})}{\text{N}{\equiv}\text{C}\underset{\overset{|}{\text{N}}}{}\underset{\text{CH}_3}{}} \qquad \underset{(\text{IV})}{\overset{\overset{\text{O}}{\|}}{\text{H}_2\text{N}-\text{C}}\underset{\overset{|}{\text{N}}}{}\overset{\overset{\text{O}}{\|}}{\text{C}}{\sim}\text{NH}_2\underset{\text{CH}_2\text{C}_6\text{H}_5}{}}$$

The 4-position in DPN$^+$ is subject to general attack by nucleophiles, such as cyanide ion, bisulfite ion, enol anions, and imidazole bases. The transfer of hydride ion from a substrate would thus be an analogous reaction. Kosower[11] has suggested that the transfer may be preceded by the formation of a charge-transfer complex in some cases and cites spectral evidence to show that the reduction of DPN$^+$ by dithionite, $S_2O_4^=$, proceeds in this way [Eq. (4)]. A rearrangement of the conjugate

11. E. M. Kosower, in P. D. Boyer, H. Lardy, and K. Myrback (eds.), *The Enzymes*, vol. 3, Academic, New York, 1960, p. 171.

acid of this complex could result in attachment of a hydrogen at the 4-position [structure (V)].

The significance of the dithionite reduction is that Karrer had shown much earlier that this reduction produced coenzyme DPNH with full enzymic activity, in contrast to that produced by other chemical methods,

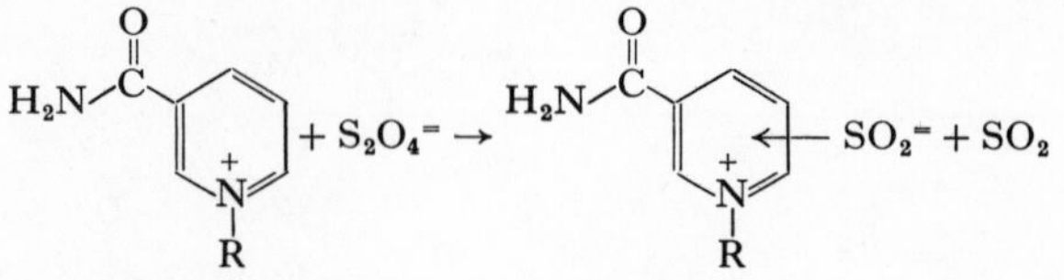

(4)

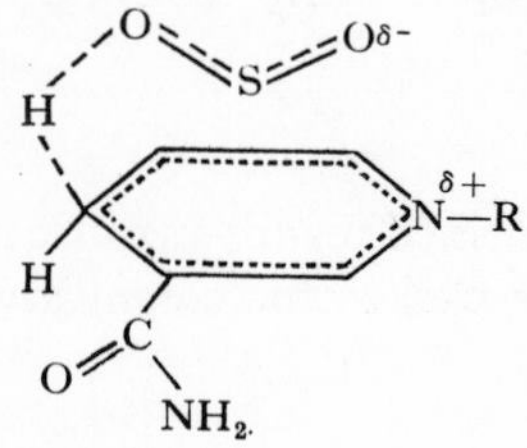

(V)

e.g., sodium borohydride reduction. The above reaction is a hydride transfer from HSO_2^- to DPN^+ to produce SO_2 and DPNH. However, explicit evidence that charge-transfer complexes are involved in the enzymic reduction is still lacking.

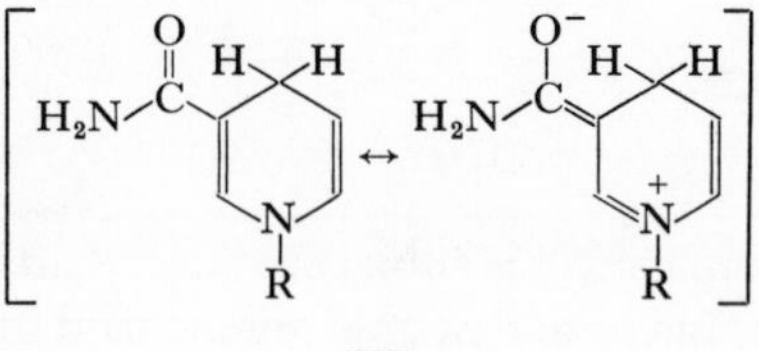

(VI)

The redox potential of DPN^+ models and their reactivities with nucleophiles, such as cyanide ion, vary with the chemical character of the group at the 3-position in the pyridine ring. Thus, the 3-acetyl derivative has a potential favoring the reduced form (compared with DPN itself), and it also has a greater affinity for cyanide ion, as indicated by the equilibrium constant for complex formation. The 3-alkyl derivatives, in contrast, do not add cyanide ion at all.[3] The 3-carboxamido group may thus be important in possessing the appropriate degree of electron-withdrawing character, since it stabilizes the DPNH by resonance of the type illustrated by (VI). The transition state for hydride transfer from substrate to DPN^+ would also be stabilized in a similar way. It is interesting that the isoelectronic carboxyl group cannot function as satisfactorily at the 3-position, presumably because its high degree of ionization in neutral solution produces the much less electronegative carboxy group. The 3-carboxamido substituent appears to be also involved in binding the DPN^+ to the enzyme active center, as shown by the stereospecific enzymic production of DPNH.

It is worth noting that, although the standard free energies of oxidation of DPNH and TPNH (to DPN^+ and TPN^+, respectively) are almost identical, the relative concentrations of the oxidized and reduced forms of these coenzymes in the organism may vary considerably.[12] For example, it was found that in liver the ratio $[DPN^+]/[DPNH] = 1.8$, whereas the ratio $[TPN^+]/[TPNH] = 0.03$. These are obviously steady-state, not equilibrium, values.

A fairly detailed structure for the transition state of the alcohol dehydrogenase–catalyzed oxidation of ethanol by DPN^+ has been presented by Kosower.[13] On the basis of spectral changes that occur when DPNH is bound to the enzyme, he concludes that an ammonium cation, probably from the ϵ-amino group in lysine, is located nearby. It is also known that Zn^{++} is a part of the active site of the enzyme and that a "hydrophobic" region, probably alkyl chains of amino acids, is implicated.[14] The latter is concerned with the orientation of the alkyl group of the substrate in the complex.

The simultaneous transfer of a hydride from the alcohol carbon to the pyridimium ring and a proton to the nitrogen of lysine provides a low-energy transition state, since the positive charge can be conveniently dispersed. In the transition state shown in Eq. (5), only the groups whose bonding is significantly altered by the oxidation are shown, the proper orientation of the reaction centers being assured by complexing with the enzyme. (Hydrogen and other complexing bonds are indicated by the symbol ‖‖; partly formed bonds in the transition state by the symbol ---.)

12. G. E. Glock and P. McLean, *Biochem. J.*, **61**, 381 (1955).
13. E. M. Kosower, *Biochim. Biophys. Acta*, **56**, 474 (1962). A detailed account of the chemistry of pyridine nucleotides is also given by Kosower in *Molecular Biochemistry*, McGraw-Hill, New York, 1962, pp. 166–219.
14. B. Vennesland and F. H. Westheimer, in W. D. McElroy and B. Glass (eds.), *Mechanism of Enzyme Action*, Johns Hopkins, Baltimore, 1954, p. 357.

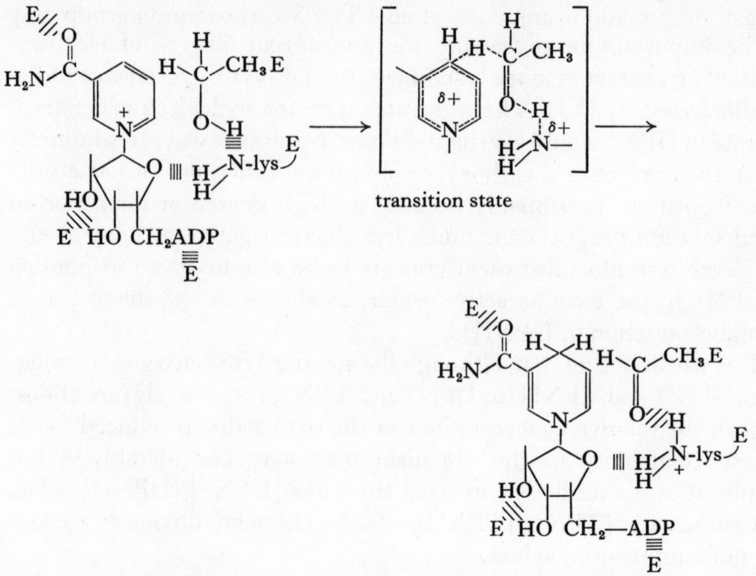

transition state

(5)

E = enzyme

FLAVIN NUCLEOTIDES

Riboflavin is the prosthetic group of the various "flavoproteins," or "yellow enzymes." The yellow enzyme of yeast, isolated by Warburg and Christian[15] in 1932, contains the coenzyme flavin mononucleotide

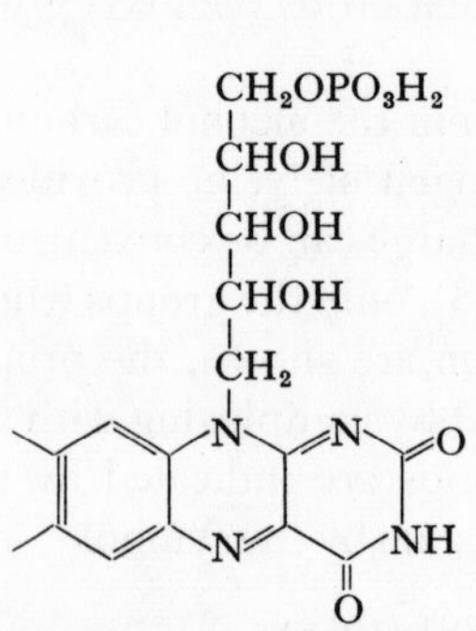

flavin mononucleotide
(VII)

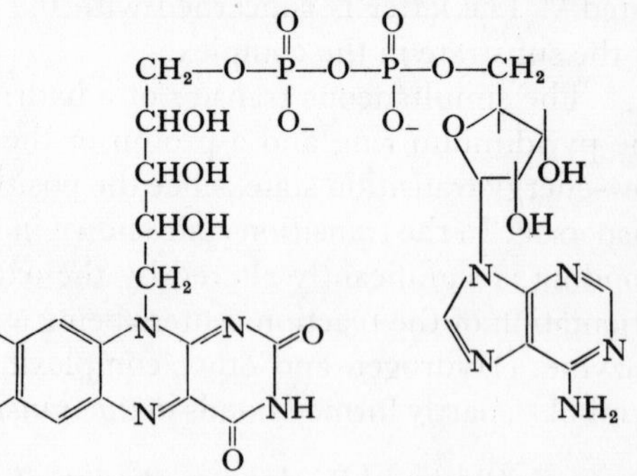

flavin adenine dinucleotide
(VIII)

(FMN), while other flavoproteins contain flavin dinucleotide (FAD) [structures (VII) and (VIII)]. Riboflavin (FMN without the phosphate group) is yellow in its normal oxidized form because of the presence of the isoalloxazine chromophore. The heterocyclic ring loses its conjugation on reduction and is converted to the colorless leuco form. Flavoproteins oxidize a very wide variety of substrates and are of great importance in metabolism. The particular protein in the enzyme modifies the potential of the flavin nucleotides and, probably more important, the activation energy of the redox reaction.

The isoalloxazine ring system of the flavin nucleotides differs from the heterocyclic ring in the DPN^+-DPNH couple in being able to react by either 1- or 2-equivalent steps. This may be an extremely important characteristic allowing the diphosphopyridine nucleotide system (2-equivalent) to be coupled to systems such as the cytochromes (1-equivalent).

Many 2-equivalent reductions of simple organic compounds take place by hydride transfer and the DPN-flavoprotein reaction is probably also a hydride reaction. The reaction between the model substances,

$$(6)$$

N^1-propyldihydronicotinamide and riboflavin is certainly consistent with a hydride mechanism.[15] One-equivalent reactions involving hydrogen usually proceed by either hydrogen-atom transfer or by electron transfer, followed by protonation. A general redox system must be able to provide pathways with low-activation energies by both 1- and 2-equivalent routes.

The key grouping in the flavin that undergoes reduction is that portion of the riboflavin moiety containing the pyrimidine ring. Addition of hydride to the nitrogen atom at the 10-position of the isoalloxazine would be aided by the dispersal of the negative charge to nitrogen and oxygen, as shown in Eq. (6). (The structures in which carbon bears a negative charge are ignored in this discussion, since their contributions to the stability of the transition state and the intermediate product will be so much less than those of the more electronegative atoms, nitrogen and oxygen.) The subsequent protonation of the nitrogen at position 1 completes the reduction. Less is known about the stereochemistry of the addition of the hydrogen in the flavin coenzymes than in the DPN system because of the rapid exchange of protons on nitrogen with those of the

15. C. H. Suelter and D. E. Metzler, *Biochim. Biophys. Acta*, **44**, 23 (1960).

solvent. The intermediate anion shown in this equation has its negative charge dispersed to one nitrogen and two oxygen atoms in the pyrimidine ring, as shown in (IX).

(IX)

Addition of hydride and proton in the reverse *order* is a rather trivial variation of this mechanism, since proton reactions on nitrogen are extremely fast. (The low basicity of the 1-nitrogen makes this a less likely order in any case.) Addition of hydride and proton in the reverse *manner*, i.e., hydride at the 1-position, is most unlikely, since the negative charge introduced to the molecule by such a hydride addition cannot be located on either of the two oxygens attached to the pyrimidine ring but must reside completely at the 10-nitrogen [structure (X)]. (Dipolar structures have also been ignored in this discussion.)

(X)

The isoalloxazine unit is also well constructed for the role of serving as a 1-equivalent redox system.[16] Addition of either a hydrogen atom or one electron would produce a type of semiquinone which is stabilized certainly by resonance and possibly by coordination to a metal atom of the enzyme. Flavin radicals have been detected in submitochondrial particles by electron-spin resonance,[17] and there is no doubt that flavin semiquinones are easily formed.[18]

It is sometimes difficult to distinguish a 1-electron transfer step from a hydrogen-atom transfer step, and some doubt exists for even such a

16. H. Beinert, in P. D. Boyer, H. Lardy, and K. Myrback (eds.), *The Enzymes*, vol. 2, Academic, New York, 1960, Chapter 10.
17. H. Beinert and R. H. Sands, *Biochem. Biophys. Res. Comm.*, 3, 41 (1960).
18. H. Beinert and R. H. Sands, in M. S. Blois, Jr., H. W. Brown, R. M. Lemmon, R. O. Lindblom, M. Weissbluth (eds.), *Free Radicals in Biological Systems*, Academic, New York, 1961, p. 17.

simple reaction as the ferrous–ferric-ion exchange reaction in aqueous solution.[19]

$$\text{Fe}^{++} \overset{e}{\frown} \text{Fe}^{3+} \rightarrow \text{Fe}^{3+} + \text{Fe}^{2+}$$

or

$$\text{Fe}^{++}\text{OH}_2 \overset{\text{H·}}{\frown} \text{H}_2\text{OFe}^{3+} \rightarrow \text{Fe}^{++}\text{OH} + \text{H}_3\text{OFe}^{3+} \rightleftharpoons \text{Fe}^{3+}\text{OH}_2 + \text{H}_2\text{OFe}^{++}$$

If one writes the equations for the addition of a hydrogen atom to the 10-nitrogen, the odd electron can be located on four atoms of the adjacent ring [Eq. (7) and structures (XI)]. These structures are analogous to those written earlier for an intermediate formed by hydride

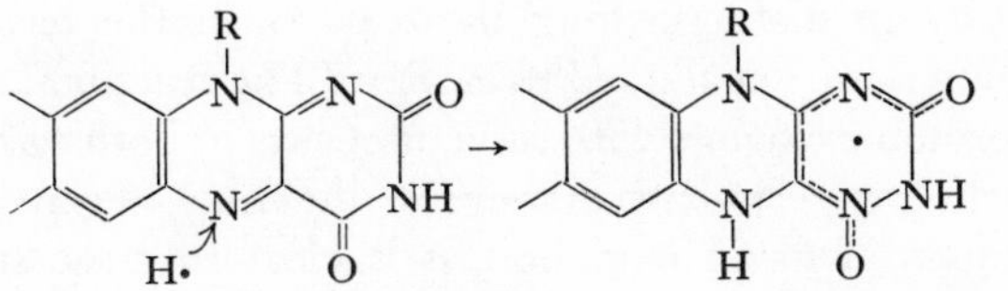

(7)

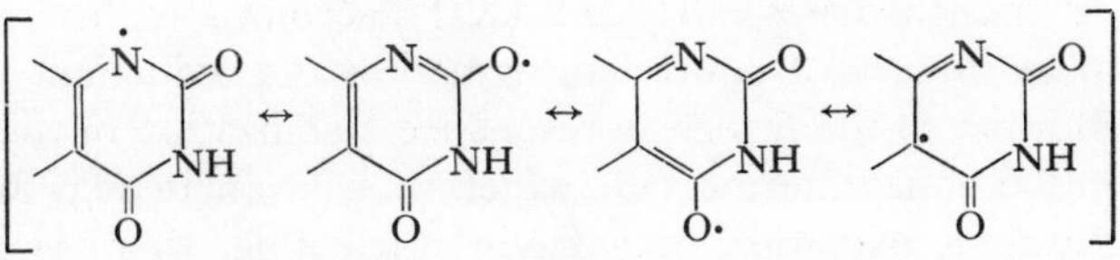

(XI)

addition, but included here is a structure with the odd electron on carbon, since electronegativity factors are of less importance in determining the energies of radicals.

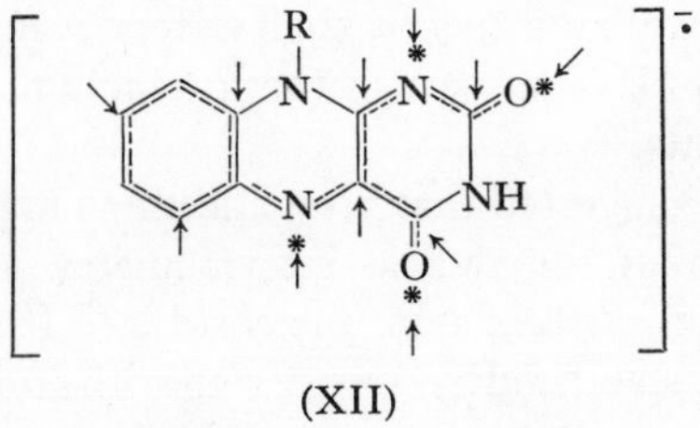

(XII)

An alternative reaction path for the 1-equivalent reduction of flavin nucleotides is the abstraction of an electron from a 1-electron donor, as occurs in the polarographic reduction. The semiquinone anion thus produced can disperse the negative charge to the two nitrogen and the

19. J. Hudis and R. W. Dodson, *J. Am. Chem. Soc.*, **78**, 911 (1956); J. Halpern, *Quart. Revs. (London)*, **1961**, 216.

two oxygen atoms [those marked with asterisks in structure (XII)]. The odd electron can be located on two nitrogen, two oxygen, and seven carbon atoms (those marked with an arrow). As before, only the electronegative atoms, nitrogen and oxygen, are considered of importance in the delocalization of the negative charge. [The pyrimidine ring in the radical-anion, structure (XII), may also exist in the tautomeric hydroxydiazine form (see Ref. 16, p. 353); however, less delocalization of charge would then be possible.]

The neutral semiquinone (XI) or the anion (XII) with which it is in equilibrium will also be formed by the oxidation of a fully reduced flavin molecule with 1-equivalent reagents. This could take place either by a hydrogen atom transfer or by a one-electron transfer to the oxidant and the difficulty in distinguishing these paths in the ferrous-ferric exchange reaction has been alluded to earlier. (The reactions are similar in that rapid proton exchange with solvent occurs in both cases making deuterium labeling experiments extremely difficult.) Regardless of the precise mechanism of flavin oxidation, it is clear that the stability of the radical intermediates, (XI) and (XII), accounts for the ease with which flavins undergo 1-equivalent oxidation and reduction.

In addition to the extensive resonance stabilization of the radical-anion (semiquinone) intermediate, which we have assumed is formed by the 1-equivalent oxidation of a flavin nucleotide, there is probably some coordination with the unpaired electrons in the transition metal atoms in the enzyme.[20, 21] The metals—chiefly iron, copper, molybdenum, and manganese—and the flavin moiety are bound to the protein in a firm complex of definite composition. The presence of the metal, however, is essential only for the interaction of the reduced flavoprotein with 1-equivalent oxidizing agents, such as ferricyanide and cytochrome b. The metal atom plays no part in the interaction of the enzyme with 2-equivalent reagents.[22]

Ingraham has suggested that aromatic rings may also be important in the stabilization of the radical intermediates produced by the 1-equivalent reduction of the flavin nucleotides.[23] It is known that alkyl radicals are partially stabilized by complexing with aromatic compounds.[24]

20. H. Beinert and R. H. Sands, Biochem. Biophys. Res. Comm., 1, 171 (1959).
21. R. C. Bray, B. G. Malmström, and T. Värngard, Biochem. J., 73, 193 (1959).
22. H. R. Mahler and D. E. Green, Science, 120, 7 (1954).
23. L. L. Ingraham, Biochemical Mechanisms, Wiley, New York, 1962, p. 78.
24. F. R. Mayo, J. Am. Chem. Soc., 75, 6133 (1953); G. S. Hammond, C. E. Boozer, C. E. Hamilton, and J. N. Sen, J. Am. Chem. Soc., 77, 3238 (1955).

CYTOCHROMES

A number of important molecules concerned with oxidation contain hemin or a closely related ring system. They include hemoglobin, catalase, peroxidase, and the cytochromes. The last are hemoproteins that differ somewhat in the way in which the hemin ring is substituted, and that differ markedly in molecular weight. (See, however, Ref. 25.) Cytochrome c, the best characterized of the four, contains one hemin group and has much the lowest molecular weight ($\sim 12,000$).

The iron atom centrally located in the porphyrin ring [structure (XIII)] plays a vital role in the transport of oxygen by hemoglobin and in the reaction with oxygen of cytochrome c, but there are important

hemin in hemoglobin and cytochrome c

(XIII)

differences between the two molecules. The peripheral groups a to h are methyl, vinyl, or carboxyethyl in the case of hemin in hemoglobin, the binding to the protein being through the carboxyl groups. The groups Y and Z, which complete the octahedral arrangement about the iron atom, are a histidine molecule (attached also to the protein) and a water molecule. The hemin in cytochrome c differs slightly in structure from that in hemoglobin in that two of the peripheral vinyl groups have become links to a peptide chain, and, an extremely important difference, the groups Y and Z are now both histidine residues [structure (XIV)]. One of the histidines turns out to be the second amino acid in the aforementioned peptide chain. Models show that the imidazole ring of the

25. R. Bomstein, R. Goldberger, and H. Tisdale, *Biochim. Biophys. Acta*, **50**, 527 (1961).

histidine is, in fact, close enough to form an iron-nitrogen bond.[26] The imidazole ring is well suited for its role as a coordinating ligand, particularly for ferric iron.

The oxygen-transporting properties of hemoglobin are associated with the octahedrally coordinated ferrous iron, just as are the reducing properties of ferrocytochrome c. The heme group in cytochrome c is buried in the protein, whereas the heme group of hemoglobin is situated at the surface of the molecule.[26, 27] Nevertheless, the iron(II) in hemo-

cytochrome c

(XIV)

globin is much more resistant to oxidation to iron(III) than is the cytochrome iron. Sutin and Christman have shown that the rate of oxidation by ferricyanide ion in aqueous buffer at room temperature is 230 times faster for Fe_{cyt}^{II} than for Fe_{hem}^{II}, despite an over-all free energy of reaction that favors the latter.[28] Since both steric and thermodynamic effects should favor hemoglobin oxidation relative to cytochrome c oxidation, it is apparent that the molecule of histidine that replaces the molecule of water as the sixth ligand of iron exerts a profound effect on the rate of oxidation.

The ferrocyanide-ferricyanide couple can be thought of as a simple model for the ferrocytochrome-ferricytochrome system. The former system, discussed in an earlier section, operates by an electron exchange. The imidazole ring in histidine also provides a conjugated framework for charge transfer between iron and the external donor or receiver.

26. A. Ehrenburg and H. Theorell, *Acta Chem. Scand.*, **9**, 1193 (1955).
27. M. F. Perutz, M. G. Rossman, A. F. Cullis, H. Muirhead, G. Will, and A. C. T. North, *Nature*, **185**, 416 (1960).
28. N. Sutin and D. R. Christman, *J. Am. Chem. Soc.*, **83**, 1773 (1961).

The porphyrin ring system in the cytochromes provides a polarizable framework for the metal cation—analogous to a solvation sphere—but one that is firmly bonded to the protein of the enzyme.

In addition to cytochrome c, three other less well characterized cytochromes are implicated in the biochemical oxidation chain. Cytochrome c_1 and cytochrome b occupy places in the chain between the flavoproteins and cytochrome c. There is considerable disagreement about the fourth major cytochrome component, however. Cytochrome oxidase, the enzyme that catalyzes the reaction between cytochrome c and molecular oxygen, may be made up of two hemoproteins, a and a_3.[29] Other evidence, however, suggests that cytochrome oxidase is a copper hemoprotein containing equivalent amounts of copper and cytochrome a.[30] (The enzyme is hereafter simply designated cytochrome a.)

Reaction with Oxygen

The over-all stoichiometry of the reaction of molecular oxygen with cytochrome c catalyzed by cytochrome oxidase involves a 4-equivalent total change [Eq. (8)].

$$4Fe^{II}_{cyt\,c} + O_2 + 4H^+ \to 4Fe^{III}_{cyt\,c} + 2H_2O \tag{8}$$

The air oxidation of ferrous ion in solution serves as the simplest model for the cytochrome-oxygen reaction. George has examined the former reaction and found the rate to be first-order in oxygen and second-order in ferrous ion.[31]

$$\frac{-d[Fe^{++}]}{dt} = k[Fe^{++}]^2\,[O_2]$$

The rate-controlling step, presumably, is the reaction of the iron(II)-oxygen complex, FeO_2^{++}, with a second ferrous ion. The species FeO_2^{++}, in which the iron atom has a formal oxidation state of six, is called *perferryl ion*. This and the corresponding enzymic form of iron is called *complex III*.

George concludes that radical mechanisms involving the exceedingly high-energy species O_2^- and HO_2 cannot account for the reaction mechanism, and he proposes the following path in which a hydrogen

29. T. Yonetani, *J. Biol. Chem.*, **236**, 1680 (1961).
30. S. Takemori, *J. Biochem.* (*Tokyo*), **47**, 382 (1960); D. E. Griffiths and D. C. Wharton, *J. Biol. Chem.*, **236**, 1850 (1961); see also M. Morrison, S. Horie, and H. S. Mason, *J. Biol. Chem.*, **238**, 2220 (1963).
31. P. George, *J. Chem. Soc.*, **1954**, 4349.

atom is transferred from the coordination shell of a ferrous ion to the perferryl ion:

$$Fe^{++} + O_2 \rightarrow FeO_2^{++}$$

$$FeO_2^{++} + H_2OFe^{++} \rightarrow FeO_2H^{++} + HOFe^{++}$$

Subsequent rapid decomposition of the ferryl ion [32] FeO_2H^{++} completes the reaction.

The formal 4-equivalent reduction of oxygen from the free state to water requires passage through the peroxy state, the latter being by no means unknown in living cells, as indicated by the ubiquity of catalase and peroxidase. The ferryl ion FeO_2H^{++} may dissociate to Fe^{3+} and HO_2^-, which, in turn, could be rapidly decomposed to oxygen again and water or act as an oxidant itself.

The uncertainty about the structure and, indeed, the composition of cytochrome a, the species known to react initially with molecular oxygen, makes a description of the cytochrome-oxygen mechanism difficult. An analogy with the ferrous-ion–oxygen reaction might be expected, but the suspected role of copper in cytochrome c–oxidase (cytochrome a) activity complicates the picture. The presence in cytochrome oxidase of iron and copper atoms with unpaired electron spins should allow rapid complex formation with oxygen, itself possessing unpaired electrons.[33]

Minnaert has measured the kinetics of the reaction between cytochrome c and molecular oxygen catalyzed by cytochrome c oxidase (cytochrome a).[34] The path shown in the following Eqs. 1 through 4 satisfies the kinetics (c·· and a·· stand for the cytochromes in the ferrous-oxidation state and c··· and a··· in the ferric):

$$c^{..} + a^{...} \rightleftharpoons c^{..}\!\!-\!\!a^{...} \qquad 1$$

$$c^{..}\!\!-\!\!a^{...} \longrightarrow c^{...}\!\!-\!\!a^{..} \qquad 2$$

$$c^{...}\!\!-\!\!a^{..} \xrightarrow{O_2} c^{...}\!\!-\!\!a^{...} \qquad 3$$

$$c^{...}\!\!-\!\!a^{...} \rightleftharpoons c^{...} + a^{...} \qquad 4$$

$$c^{..} \xrightarrow{O_2} c^{...}$$

32. M. G. Evans, P. George, and N. Uri, *Trans. Faraday Soc.*, **45**, 230 (1949).
33. For more extensive discussion of hemin model systems, see F. H. Westheimer, in P. D. Boyer, H. Lardy, and K. Myrback (eds.), *The Enzymes*, vol. 1, Academic, New York, 1959, p. 291.
34. K. Minnaert, *Biochim. Biophys. Acta*, **50**, 23 (1961); see also L. Smith and H. Conrad, *Arch. Biochem. Biophys.*, **63**, 403 (1956), and E. C. Slater, *Biochem. Soc. Symposium*, **15**, 76 (1958).

Steps 1 and 4 are complex association and dissociation, respectively. Step 2 is an electron transfer within the complex, facilitated by the polarizable groups about the metal atoms. In order to avoid formation of very high-energy species, such as O_2^- and HO_2, step 3 must be accompanied by oxidation of a second ferrous atom.

$$2Fe^{II} + O_2 + 2H^+ \rightarrow 2Fe^{III} + H_2O_2$$

The oxidized form of cytochrome c, c$\cdots$, is reoxidized with another 1-equivalent system, cytochrome c_1, which, in turn, is reoxidized by either cytochrome b or coenzyme Q, and so on, back to DPNH or succinate. The peroxide can be either rapidly decomposed to water and oxygen by the action of catalase, or it can act as an oxidant of a suitable substrate itself, under the influence of peroxidase.

COENZYME Q

Various benzoquinones with very long isoprenoid side chains have recently been shown to be implicated in physiological oxidations.[35, 36] The side chain varies in length from the six isoprene units shown in structure (XV) (coenzyme Q_6) to the ten units generally found in animal

(XV)

tissues (coenzyme Q_{10}). The lengthy unsaturated side chain is not conjugated and hence does not function as a charge-transfer link. It does, however, make the compound water-insoluble but lipid-soluble. In addition, the first double bond of the side chain may participate in the oxidation-reduction reactions of the ring. [See Eq. (9).]

Quinones may serve as either 1- or 2-equivalent oxidants, but their ability to form true semiquinones by addition of one electron is their salient characteristic. Both this reaction and the reduction to the corresponding hydroquinone are rapid and reversible processes in aqueous

35. R. L. Lester, Y. Hatefi, C. Widner, and F. L. Crane, *Biochim. Biophys. Acta*, **33**, 169 (1959); R. A. Morton, G. M. Wilson, J. S. Lowe, and W. M. F. Leat, *Chem. & Ind.* (*London*), **1957**, 1649; J. M. Hafkenscheid, J. Links, and E. C. Slater, *Biochim. Biophys. Acta*, **70**, 202 (1963).
36. *Quinones in Electron Transport* (Ciba Foundation Symposium), eds. G. E. W. Wolstenholme and C. M. O'Connor, J. and A. Churchill, Ltd., London, 1961.

solution and, presumably, in the lipid medium with which it is associated in the cell. These, then, are systems for which the term *potential* is a most appropriate one to describe reactivity.

The alkyl and alkoxyl substituents on the quinone affect the oxidation-reduction potential of the quinone-hydroquinone couple, and they undoubtedly have an important effect on the quinone-semiquinone and semiquinone-hydroquinone couples, since it has been shown that the unpaired electron in methyl and methoxyl semibenzoquinones interacts with the substituent protons.[37] Hyperconjugative-valence bond structures, like those in (XVI) and (XVII) can be used to depict the interaction between the spins of the electron and the hydrogen nuclei.

(XVI)   (XVII)

A 2-equivalent reduction of the quinone can be written in which one of the methoxy groups and the first double bond in the side chain participate[38] [Eq. (9)]. Intermediate cations, like (I) in this equation, may be important intermediates in phosphorylation reactions.[38]

(9)

37. Y. Matsunaga and C. A. McDowell, *Can. J. Chem.*, **38**, 1159 (1960).
38. V. M. Clark and A. Todd, Ref. 36, p. 190.

Coenzyme Q and its reduced form are links in what is called the *electron-transport chain*, appearing between the flavoproteins (1- or 2-equivalent reagents) and cytochrome c_1 (a 1-equivalent reagent).

$$\text{(naphthalene structure)} + R-O-\overset{\overset{O}{\|}}{\underset{\underset{OH}{|}}{P}}-OH + Br_2 \rightarrow$$

$$\text{(naphthoquinone structure)} + R-O-\overset{\overset{O}{\|}}{\underset{\underset{OH}{|}}{P}}-O-\overset{\overset{O}{\|}}{\underset{\underset{OH}{|}}{P}}-OH + 2HBr \qquad R = \text{adenosine} \qquad (10)$$

Quinones such as Coenzyme Q may be intimately involved in oxidative phosphorylation.[39] For example, the laboratory synthesis of adenosine diphosphate (ADP) has been accomplished by oxidizing a

$$\text{(naphthalene structure with } O-P-OR) + H_3PO_4 + Br_2 \rightarrow$$

$$\text{(naphthoquinone structure)} + R-O-\overset{\overset{O}{\|}}{\underset{\underset{OH}{|}}{P}}-O-\overset{\overset{O}{\|}}{\underset{\underset{OH}{|}}{P}}-OH + 2HBr \qquad (11)$$

naphthoquinol phosphate by bromine[40] in the presence of adenosine-5' phosphate (AMP)[41] [Eq. (10)]. Alternatively, ADP may be produced by the oxidation of the naphthoquinol ester of AMP in the presence of inorganic phosphate[41] [Eq. (11)].

39. See however R. E. Beyer, W. M. Noble, and T. J. Hirschfeld, *Can. J. Biochem. and Physiol.*, **40**, 511 (1962).
40. Bromine-oxidation mechanisms are discussed on page 131.
41. V. M. Clark, D. W. Hutchinson, and A. Todd, *J. Chem. Soc.*, **1961**, 722.

In a similar way adenosine triphosphate, ATP, has been prepared by the bromine oxidation of the pyrophosphate diester of the naphthoquinol and adenosine in the presence of phosphate ions.[42]

The oxidative phosphorylation mechanisms occurring here can be rationalized in terms of production of an active phosphorylating species, such as a metaphosphate[42] formed by a hydride removal by the oxidant (or removal of an electron pair, if the quinol anion is shown to be the oxidized species), and a simultaneous heterolysis of the quinol-ester bond [Eq. (12)].

$$\text{(12)}$$

Alternatively, the displacement by phosphate might be coupled to the oxidation step [Eq. (13)].

$$\text{(13)}$$

BIOCHEMICAL MACHINES

The term *biochemical machine* has been used to describe the action of the mitochondrion in converting to utilizable chemical energy the energy released by the oxidation of organic molecules.[43] Mitochondria are subcellular bodies of characteristic oblong shape present in the oxygen-consuming cells of animals and plants. In a chemical sense, their function is twofold. First, by providing suitable enzyme and

42. Todd, *Proc. Chem. Soc.*, **1962**, 199; see also A. Lapidot and D. Samuel, *Biochim. Biophys. Acta*, **65**, 164 (1962).
43. D. E. Green and Y. Hatefi, *Science*, **133**, 13 (1961).

coenzyme systems, they can make the oxidation of organic substrates by molecular oxygen take place rapidly.

$$C_6H_{12}O_6 + 6O_2 \rightarrow 6CO_2 + 6H_2O$$

Molecular oxygen usually reacts readily only by radical, 1-equivalent mechanisms, whereas saturated aliphatic organic substrates prefer 2-equivalent steps. The intervention of catalytic species (see principle of equi-valence change, Chapter 2) lowers the exorbitant activation energy of the direct glucose-combustion reaction to an extremely low value.

The second and in a real sense the "vital" function of the highly organized enzyme and coenzyme arrangement within the mitochondria is to utilize the energy available from the oxidation reaction to accomplish a chemical synthesis, that of adenosine triphosphate, ATP.

It is well-known that hydrolysis of ATP to adenosine diphosphate and inorganic phosphate liberates energy, and that this energy may appear in the form of mechanical, osmotic, chemical, or electrical work. The energy released in this way (and hence the energy required to form ATP from its components) amounts to about 12 kcal mole^{-1}. The energy available from the complete oxidation of 1 mole of glucose is about 690 kcal, most of this energy being released by the oxidation of pyruvic acid,

$$CH_3\overset{\overset{\displaystyle O}{\|}}{C}CO_2H,$$ two molecules of which are formed from one of glucose via lactic acid.

The degradation of pyruvic acid to 3 moles of carbon dioxide and 2 moles of water takes place by a series of 2-equivalent steps in the Krebs citric acid cycle. The cycle operates by producing a mole of DPNH from DPN$^+$ (or, in one step, a mole of reduced flavin nucleotide) for every formal 2-equivalent change in the oxidation state of the substrate. Each oxidation step in the citric acid cycle, with one exception, provides enough energy to synthesize 3 moles of ATP. The exception is the conversion of succinic acid to fumaric acid, in which a flavin nucleotide is the oxidant rather than DPN$^+$. In this case only 2 moles of ATP can be synthesized, since, as will be seen from the subsequent discussion, the DPNH-flavin reaction itself is coupled to ATP synthesis.

The DPNH-oxygen reaction releases some 52 kcal mole^{-1} of reactants.

$$DPNH + \tfrac{1}{2}O_2 + H^+ \rightarrow DPN^+ + H_2O$$

The direct reaction between these reagents is very slow and intermediates, such as the flavin nucleotides and the cytochromes, are involved in the reaction as catalytic species to lower the activation energy and speed the reaction. Of equal or greater importance is the fact that three oxidative phosphorylation steps (each storing 12 kcal of potential energy) are included in the sequence.

The mechanism of the oxidation sequence has been fairly well elucidated, but the way in which the ADP to ATP reaction is coupled to the several steps is still not clear (see the previous section, however). Various reagents can be used to uncouple the latter synthesis from the oxidation reactions, but it is believed that the same general mechanisms apply in the sense that the sequence of components are the same in the coupled and uncoupled oxidations.[43, 44] The energy, of course, appears in the form of heat when the ATP synthesis is eliminated.

If we take that portion of the citric acid cycle in which malic acid is oxidized to oxaloacetic acid, the following tentative, and somewhat simplified, mechanistic picture emerges [Eq. (14)]. The malic acid probably transfers a hydride ion to DPN^+ to form DPNH. [The coenzyme only is shown in Eq. (14).] The DPNH is reoxidized by a flavoprotein, again probably by hydride transfer. The reduced flavin, shown as the anion in Eq. (14), can reduce two units of ferricytochrome c. This is accomplished with the intervention of coenzyme Q, cytochromes b and c_1 and some non-heme iron species and is the cross-over point in the sequence where 2-equivalent reactions are replaced by 1-equivalent reactions, probably electron transfers. The reduced cytochrome c is in turn oxidized by ferricytochrome a, and the chain finally terminates with the reaction of ferrocytochrome a with oxygen to form water.

malic acid, DPN, flavin, coenzyme Q, cyt b, Fe, cyt c_1, cyt c, cyt a, O_2

The dotted lines in these equations indicate that the reaction proceeds via intermediates and not directly. Even in the case of the DPNH-flavin reaction, of course, the coupled ATP synthesis should be considered. [Only the location in the chain of the oxidative phosphorylations are indicated in Eq. (14).] The coupling of the oxidative and phosphorylative processes occurs in mitochondrial units having a particular membrane arrangement[45]; the elucidation of the precise mechanism of this coupling is one of the most intriguing problems facing the biochemist.

Some of the large molecular weight components of the oxidation chain (flavoproteins and some of the cytochromes) are embedded in a protein-lipid matrix and are virtually immobile. The smaller components, such as DPN, coenzyme Q, oxygen, and cytochrome c have

44. A. W. Linnane and E. B. Titchner, *Biochim. Biophys. Acta*, **39**, 469 (1960).
45. D. M. Ziegler, A. W. Linnane, D. E. Green, C. M. S. Dass, and H. Ris, *Biochim. Biophys. Acta*, **28**, 524 (1958); D. E. Green and T. Oda, *J. Biochem. (Tokyo)*, **49**, 742 (1961).

H$_2$NC=O + $\overset{OH}{\underset{CH_2CO_2H}{CHCO_2H}}$ + N$^+$-R $\longrightarrow$ H$_2$NC=O + $\overset{O=C-CO_2H}{CH_2CO_2H}$ + H$^+$

(various intermediate flavin and dihydronicotinamide structures with R—N, N—R, NH, O, CH$_3$ substituents)

+ 2Fe$_{cyt\,c}^{III}$ $\dashrightarrow$ + 2Fe$_{cyt\,c}^{II}$ (+ATP)

2Fe$_{cyt\,c}^{II}$ + $\tfrac{1}{2}$O$_2$ $\dashrightarrow$ 2Fe$_{cyt\,c}^{III}$ + H$_2$O (+ATP)

HO$_2$CCHOHCH$_2$CO$_2$H + $\tfrac{1}{2}$O$_2$ $\longrightarrow$ HO$_2$CCCH$_2$CO$_2$H + H$_2$O (+3ATP)

155

sufficient mobility within the lipid phase to interact readily with them by conventional means. The 1-equivalent reactions between the less mobile cytochromes are doubtless electron transfers facilitated by the molecules' juxtaposition within the matrix. However, the terms *electron flow* and *electron transport chain* that are often used to describe the oxidation sequence may be somewhat misleading; they rather suggest that some form of electrical conduction is the mechanism of *all* the coupled oxidation steps that are ingeniously arranged in sequence by the enzyme complex of the mitochondrion.

LIPOIC ACID

The sulfhydryl group —SH and the disulfide group —SS— form one of the most common oxidation-reduction couples in biological systems.[46] One of these, lipoic acid [structure (XIX)],[47] also known

$$H_2C \underset{CH_2}{\overset{S-S}{\diagup}} CH-(CH_2)_4CO_2H$$

lipoic acid

(XIX)

as thioctic acid, is a cofactor involved in the oxidative decarboxylation of pyruvic acid. Cyclic disulfides should be convenient cofactors in biochemical oxidations because of the facile ring-opening and -closing reactions made possible by the highly polarizable sulfur atoms [Eq. (15)].

Ring opening and closing can both occur via nucleophilic displacements on sulfur, ring strain being not unduly great in the five-membered

$$N: \underset{CH_2}{\overset{S-S}{\diagup}} CH(CH_2)_4CO_2H \rightleftharpoons H_2C \underset{CH_2}{\overset{\overset{+}{N}-S \quad S^-}{\diagup}} CH(CH_2)_4CO_2H \quad (15)$$

46. For an extensive account of these reactions, see P. D. Boyer, in P. D. Boyer, H. Lardy, and K. Myrback (eds.), *The Enzymes*, vol. 1, Academic, New York, 1959, p. 511.
47. L. J. Reed, in P. D. Boyer, H. Lardy, and K. Myrback (eds.), *The Enzymes*, vol. 3, Academic, New York, 1959, p. 195; I. C. Gunsalus, in W. D. McElroy and B. Glass (eds.), *Mechanism of Enzyme Action*, Johns Hopkins, Baltimore, 1954, p. 545.

ring.[48] This reaction is of importance in the oxidative decarboxylation of pyruvic acid[49] in the Krebs cycle. In this, as shown in Eqs. (16), the cofactors coenzyme A, lipoic acid, thiamine pyrophosphate, and DPN+ are involved in the conversion of pyruvic acid (I) and oxalacetic acid (VII) to citric acid (VIII) and carbon dioxide. Several nucleophilic displacements by and on sulfur take place, as can be seen. (In the equations of Chart I only the functional groups involved in the reactions of the cofactors are shown, i.e., thiamine pyrophosphate is abbreviated

as coenzyme A as CoASH, and lipoic acid as

The decarboxylation is accomplished upon formation of the unstable compound (III) formed by reaction of pyruvic acid with the ylid of thiamine pyrophosphate (II). (Breslow[50] has shown by means of deuterium-exchange experiments that (II) will be formed readily from thiamine without alkali being required[51] [Eq. (17)].) The product (IV) is

$$\text{} \quad (17)$$

a nucleophile which displaces sulfur from sulfur in a molecule of lipoic acid to form (V). This then regenerates the ylid of thiamine pyrophosphate once more and acetyl dihydrolipoic acid (VI). The nucleophilic sulfhydryl

48. J. A. Barltrop, P. M. Hayes, and M. Calvin, *J. Am. Chem. Soc.*, **76**, 4348 (1954); A. Fava, A. Iliceto, and E. Camera, *J. Am. Chem. Soc.*, **79**, 833 (1957); L. S. Levitt, *Science*, **118**, 696 (1953).
49. L. J. Reed, *Physiol. Revs.*, **33**, 544 (1953).
50. R. Breslow, *J. Am. Chem. Soc.*, **79**, 1762 (1957).
51. The effect of electron-withdrawing atoms (such as N and S in thiamine) on ionization of carbon acids is interesting. One would expect that, the greater the number of electron-withdrawing groups, the greater would be the stability of the carbanion. With aromatic carbon acids, however, a competition occurs between proton loss and hydroxide-ion addition. Thus, 1,3,5-trinitrobenzene does not exchange its aromatic protons in basic solution, but 1,3-dinitrobenzene does. (R. J. Pollitt and B. C. Saunders, *Proc. Chem. Soc.*, **1962**, 176). The stability

of and

results from the juxtaposition of the negative charge and the electron-withdrawing groups. The presence of more of the latter would, presumably, simply stabilize the hydroxyl-ion adduct.

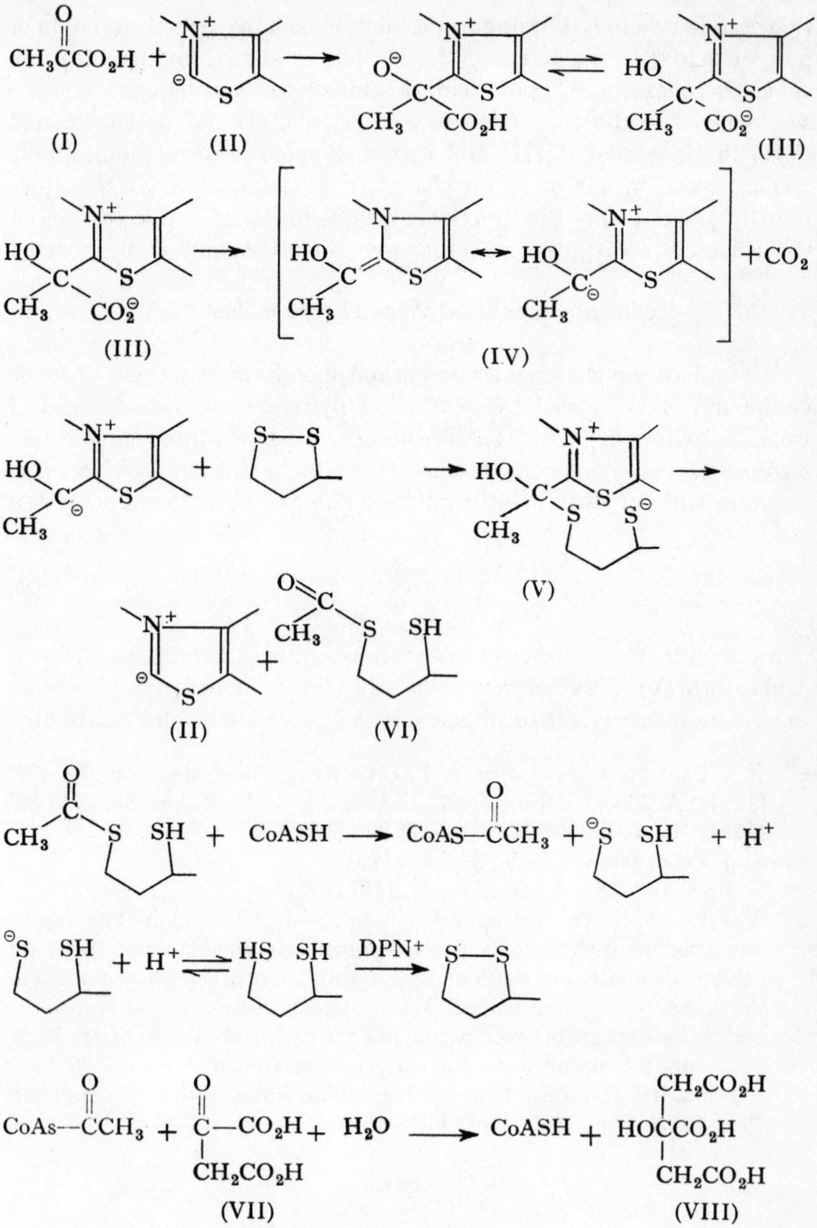

Chart I

group of coenzyme A[52] reacts with the carbonyl carbon of VI and eliminates the sulfur anion of dihydrolipoic acid, which, in turn, is oxidized by DPN^+ to regenerate lipoic acid. The acetyl coenzyme A adds to the carbonyl group of oxalacetic acid (VII) to give the coenzyme A derivative of citric acid, which is then hydrolyzed to citric acid (VIII) and regenerated coenzyme A.

SOME HYDROXYLATION REACTIONS

Systems that are able to hydroxylate aromatic compounds invariably contain ions of metals, such as copper or iron. The oxidants are usually hydrogen peroxide or molecular oxygen, and the two metals form analogous complexes with these oxidants. Ferrous ion combines with oxygen to form the perferryl ion FeO_2^{++},[31] in which the iron has a formal oxidation state of +6. The term *complex III* is frequently used to describe this state.

$$Fe^{++} + O_2 \rightarrow FeO_2^{++}$$

On the other hand, ferrous ion and hydrogen peroxide, the well-known Fenton's reagent, combine to give free hydroxyl radicals.[53]

$$Fe^{++} + H_2O_2 \rightarrow FeOH^{++} + HO\cdot$$

The ion FeO_2H^{++},[32, 54] often called *complex I*, is formed by the reaction of ferric ion with hydrogen peroxide.

$$Fe^{3+} + H_2O_2 \rightarrow FeO_2H^{++} + H^+$$

The analogous copper ion CuO_2H^+ is similarly formed.

$$Cu^{++} + H_2O_2 \rightarrow CuO_2H^+ + H^+$$

Brackman and Havinga[55] have studied the ortho hydroxylation of phenol by cupric-ion–amine–hydrogen peroxide mixtures as a model for tyrosinase activity, since this copper-containing enzyme catalyzes the

52. L. Jaenicke and F. Lynen, in P. D. Boyer, H. Lardy, and K. Myrback (eds.), *The Enzymes*, vol. 3, Academic, New York, 1960, p. 42.
53. See Refs. 47 and 48, Chapter 3.
54. J. A. Christiansen, *Acta Chem. Scand.*, **9**, 272 (1955); B. A. Chance and R. R. Ferguson, in W. D. McElroy and B. Glass (eds.), *Mechanism of Enzyme Action*, Johns Hopkins, Baltimore, 1954, p. 389.
55. W. Brackman and E. Havinga, *Rec. trav. chim.*, **74**, 1107 (1955).

ortho hydroxylation of the phenol tyrosine by oxygen. They suggest that the copper-phenol complex, I in Eq. (18), decomposes by a concerted cyclic 2-equivalent mechanism, in which the hydroxyl group and hydrogen atom exchange positions. An attractive modification of their mechanism can be written, which is essentially an assisted electrophilic aromatic substitution[56] [Eq. (18)].

$$(18)$$

The ability of cupric ion–hydrogen peroxide systems to hydroxylate phenol and aniline in the ortho positions does suggest attack by an electrophile, such as HO^+. However, benzene can be converted to phenol and benzoic acid to salicylic acid by these reagents,[57] and an electron-deficient species similar to HO^+ might be expected to discriminate drastically between these substrates.

Breslow and Lukens[58] have studied the hydroxylation of various aromatic compounds by ferrous ion, ascorbic acid, and either hydrogen peroxide or molecular oxygen. They obtained evidence that the hydroxylating agent is the hydroxyl radical rather than some more electrophilic species. (The perhydroxyl radical HO_2 has also been suggested as the electrophile in metabolite hydroxylations.[59]) Ascorbic acid can function as a 1-equivalent reductant because of the stability of the intermediate radical (page 113). When oxygen is the oxidant rather than hydrogen peroxide, the hydrogen peroxide required is generated by the ferrous-ion–catalyzed autoxidation of ascorbic acid.

A 1-equivalent oxidation of an aromatic compound by hydrogen peroxide that does not result in hydroxylation is the cupric-ion–catalyzed oxidation of catechol to the semiquinone[60] [Eq. (19)].

56. L. L. Ingraham, *Biochemical Mechanisms*, Wiley, New York, 1962, p. 72.
57. J. O. Konecny, *J. Am. Chem. Soc.*, **76**, 4993 (1954).
58. R. Breslow and L. N. Lukens, *J. Biol. Chem.*, **235**, 292 (1960).
59. R. O. C. Norman and G. K. Radda, *Proc. Chem. Soc.*, **1962**, 138.
60. L. L. Ingraham, *Arch. Biochem. Biophys.*, **81**, 309 (1959).

The existence of organic radicals in many other oxidase systems has been suspected, and in many cases electron-spin resonance signals have been detected.[61] Isenberg has recently pointed out that caution must be used in attributing broad electron-spin resonance signals to the presence

$$Cu^{++} + H_2O_2 \rightarrow CuO_2H^+ + H^+$$

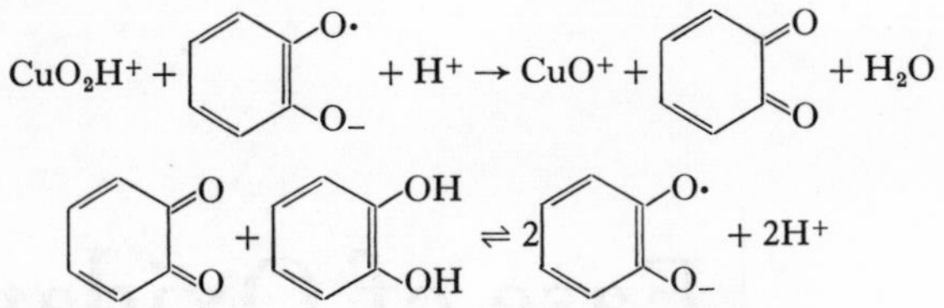

(19)

of organic radicals, since extensive corrections must be made for inorganic trace components. Organic radical concentrations may be overestimated by as much as 500 times, if only a direct comparison with the paramagnetic standard is made.[62]

Photosensitized oxygenation is proving to be a particularly useful way of introducing hydroxyl groups into natural products,[63] for example,[64]

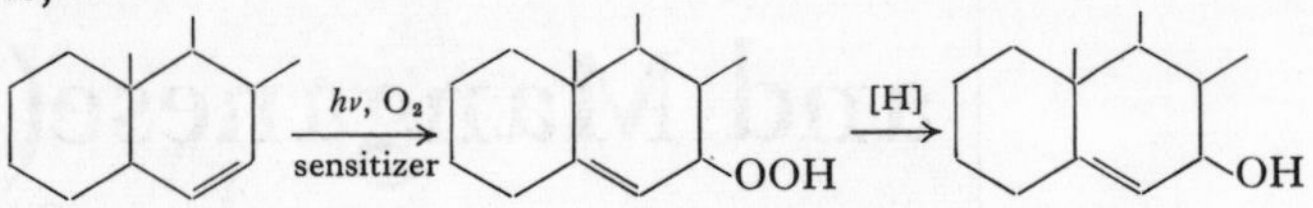

Little oxygenation occurs if the olefin lacks allylic hydrogens, or if the sensitizer (a porphyrin in the case above) is omitted. This oxygenation has been found to be highly stereospecific with the new C—O bond being cis to the C—H bond that is broken. The mechanism, then, probably involves formation of a cyclic six-membered transition state between the olefin and an activated oxygen molecule [Eq. (20)].

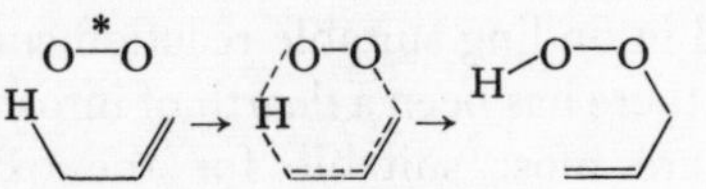

(20)

Photooxygenation appears to be involved in the biosynthesis of many other natural products.[65]

61. See, for example, I. Yamazaki and L. H. Piette, *Biochim. Biophys. Acta,* **50**, 62 (1961).
62. I. Isenberg, *Biochem. Biophys. Res. Comm.,* **5**, 139 (1961).
63. G. O. Schenck, *Angew. Chem.,* **69**, 579 (1957).
64. A. Nickon and J. F. Bagli, *J. Am. Chem. Soc.,* **83**, 1498 (1961).
65. See, for example, A. I. Scott and C. T. Bedford, *J. Am. Chem. Soc.,* **84**, 2271 (1962).

Ease of Oxidation of Functional Group by Chromium(VI) and Manganese(VII)

Some of the reagents whose oxidation mechanisms have been discussed in this book are highly specific and restrict their activity to a few functional groups. The specificity of such reagents as periodic acid and selenium dioxide, for example, is well-known, and little difficulty is usually experienced in finding suitable reaction conditions for their use. On the other hand, there has been a dearth of information on the reaction conditions which are most suitable for the oxidation of particular functional groups by the more general and more powerful reagents chromium(VI) and manganese(VII).

The mechanism studies that have been referred to in the body of the text allow some generalizations to be made, which may be of use in synthetic work.

Chromic Acid

Chromic acid oxidizes hydrocarbons, alcohols, aldehydes, ethers, olefins, and glycols. The structural features in the substrate that speed its oxidation by this reagent are summarized in Table A-1. Alcohols

Table A-1 *Effect of structural features on rate of chromic acid and permanganate oxidations*

Oxidation	Functional group	Substitution[a]	Electron-withdrawing substituents[b]
Chromic acid	—C̶—H	Accelerates	Decelerates
	$>$CHOH	Little effect	Decelerates
	—C$\diagup^{O}_{\diagdown H}$		Accelerates
	—ĊHOH —ĊHOH	Accelerates	Decelerates
Permanganate	—Ċ—H	Accelerates	Decelerates
	$>$CHOH	Little effect	Accelerates
	—C$\diagup^{O}_{\diagdown H}$		Little effect in neutral solution Greatly accelerates in basic solution
	$>$C=C$<$ [c]	Decelerates	Decelerates

[a] This refers to the effect of replacing hydrogens at the free bonds with alkyl groups.

[b] This refers to the effect of substituting an electron-withdrawing group on an alkyl or aryl group already attached to the functional group.

[c] The effect of reaction conditions on the product distribution in this reaction is discussed in Chapter 5.

normally are oxidized much faster than hydrocarbons, ethers, or aldehydes. However, the aromatic aldehyde and aromatic alcohol reactions have rho values of opposite sign, and electron-withdrawing groups in the substrates will speed aldehyde oxidations but slow alcohol oxidations.

All chromic acid oxidations are acid-catalyzed, and there appears to be little advantage in changing acidity in order to encourage the oxidation of one functional group at the expense of another. Changing the solvent can alter relative reactivities, however, since it is known that alcohol oxidations proceed very much faster in acetic acid than in water, whereas aldehyde oxidations are only slightly accelerated by this change.

Permanganate

Permanganate will oxidize virtually any organic molecule, but the reaction velocity is sharply affected by changes in the substrate and in the reaction conditions, particularly in the pH of the medium. The latter has been water in virtually all the cases that have been closely examined.

The relative ease of oxidation of alcohol and aldehyde groups can often be inverted by altering the pH. For example, the rate constants for the permanganate oxidation of C_6H_5CHO and $(C_6H_5)_2CHOH$ are approximately equal at pH 12. At pH 12.8 the alcohol is oxidized at about seven times the rate of the aldehyde; at pH 11 the effect is just about reversed. This is because aldehydes, both aliphatic and aromatic, are oxidized at reasonable rates even in neutral solution, whereas alcohols are oxidized rapidly only via their alkoxide ions. Electron-withdrawing groups have a great accelerating effect on the oxidation of both alcohols and aldehydes, but particularly with the latter.

Subject Index

165

Author Index